Practical
CONSERVATION
GRASSLANDS, HEATHS AND MOORS

ANDREW LANE

THE OPEN UNIVERSITY IN ASSOCIATION WITH THE
NATURE CONSERVANCY COUNCIL

Hodder & Stoughton

LONDON SYDNEY AUCKLAND

Practical CONSERVATION

Open University Course Team

Andrew Lane (Course Team Chair)

Susan Carr (Lecturer)

Pamela Furniss (Project Officer)

Jennie Moffatt (Course Manager)

Graham Turner (BBC Producer)

Amanda Smith (Editor)

Lesley Passey (Designer)

Keith Howard (Graphic Artist)

Roy Lawrance (Graphic Artist)

Jeff Edwards (Cartographer)

Bernie Lake (Secretary)

ISBN 0 340 53370 6

First published 1992
Copyright © The Open University 1992

Designed by the Graphic Design Group of The Open University

Typeset by The Open University

Printed in the United Kingdom for the educational division of Hodder and Stoughton Ltd, Mill Road, Dunton Green, Sevenoaks, Kent by Butler & Tanner Ltd, Frome and London

Contents

Foreword

This book is produced by The Open University as part of the *Practical Conservation* training programme which deals with all aspects of conservation on land that is managed largely for commercial or recreational purposes (see Figure 0.1).

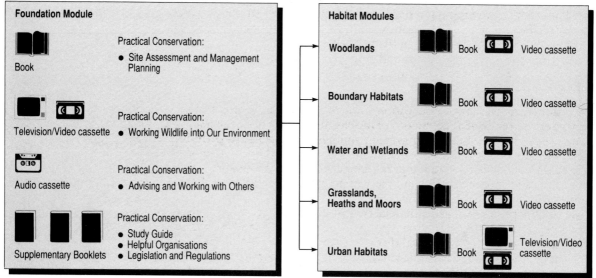

Figure 0.1
The Open University teaching programme for Practical Conservation

The foundation module covers site assessment and land use management planning in general and includes:

▶ the foundation book;

▶ a video cassette of a 50 minute television programme;

▶ a 60 minute audio cassette;

▶ two supplementary booklets;

▶ a *Study Guide* to the full programme.

This book with its accompanying 30 minute video cassette forms one of a series of modules on practical aspects of conservation management for a range of habitats:

▶ Woodlands;

▶ Boundary Habitats;

▶ Water and Wetlands;

▶ Grasslands, Heaths and Moors;

▶ Urban Habitats.

These training materials are suitable for use by groups or by individuals, studying alone or in association with a formal course. For those who would like to gain practical experience or a qualification, The Open University training programme is being incorporated into courses offered by colleges, field centres and other training bodies.

For further information please write to: Learning Materials Sales Office, The Open University, PO Box 188, Walton Hall, Milton Keynes MK7 6DH.

Chapter 1

INTRODUCTION

Grasslands, heaths and moors cover more than 45% of Great Britain. They range from intensively managed, temporary grass leys through permanent grasslands which are more than five years old to unimproved, rough grazing areas. They are a dominant feature of much of the countryside, giving colour to the landscape in between the lines and shapes drawn by roads, rivers, hedgerows, villages, towns and cities. They also provide a variety of habitats for wildlife, as well as being a significant resource for the land manager or owner.

The commercial uses and conservation value of grasslands, heaths and moors depend on the characteristics of the site and how it has been managed in the past. The biggest use is for grazing animals of various sorts including wild game animals, but there are also many areas devoted to amenity or recreational uses such as country parks, golf courses and sports fields. Some areas are used for both grazing and recreation, particularly much of the common land in England and Wales or uncultivated areas in Scotland. However, the priorities for commercial management and for conservation can conflict, particularly when the land manager is not aware of their interactions. This book is a practical guide on how to integrate wildlife and landscape conservation with grassland, heath and moor management for grazing, game or recreational purposes, to provide the most satisfactory outcome for all these interests. It should be used by all those who have, or would like to have, an active involvement in managing the countryside or other areas with conservation potential, including farmers, advisers, students, conservation volunteers, planners, countryside rangers and park wardens, and by school teachers and interested members of the general public.

Grasslands, heaths and moors may form a large part of the British countryside but they are also subject to many changes, particularly from agricultural developments. Some areas are managed exclusively for commercial purposes, with little or no consideration for wildlife. The conservation value of these areas is increasingly being recognised and acted on while the amount of land that needs to be intensively managed is declining because of agricultural overproduction. There are therefore tremendous opportunities now to improve on past management, while maintaining the best existing areas, and to create new grasslands and heathlands, which is encouraged by more favourable government policies.

1.1   Grassland, heath and moor management

Virtually all of the grasslands, heaths and moors in Great Britain have been managed or influenced by human activities in the past, and still need to be managed to maintain or develop their inherent value. Increasingly, as for all forms of land use, this means producing a management plan to assess the best management options. A management plan also helps to cope with the complexity of running a modern business and to maintain continuity and consistency for long-term operations such as conservation, game sports and forestry.

Management planning in general is dealt with in the foundation module. The five main stages in the development of a plan are summarised in Figure 1.2. of the foundation book. Stage 1 integrates landscape and wildlife conservation assessment with a consideration of the business aspects of land use, e.g. grazing livestock, rearing game, recreation; Stage 2 identifies the land manager's objectives and the relevant constraints; Stage 3 involves exploring and choosing the options for achieving the objectives identified; in Stage 4 a formal plan of action is drafted; and Stage 5 puts the plan into practice and monitors progress.

Unless the area of land under consideration consists solely of grassland, heath or moor, it is good practice to develop a general management plan for the area before going on to consider the place of grassland, heath or moor within it. This becomes particularly important if you are thinking, for example, of creating a new area of herb-rich grassland. Under these circumstances you first need to answer the question 'Is grassland an appropriate use of this site?' If the site is already valuable for wildlife, for example as wetland, cultivating the soil and sowing a grass seed mixture would result in a net conservation loss. For any new area, you should only proceed if the general management plan indicates that, *all things considered*, it is the best use of the land.

This book and the associated video cassette concentrate on three particular aspects of management planning – assessment (Stage 1), management options (Stage 3) and implementation (Stage 5). If you are preparing a management plan, or if you already have one, they will help you to put it into practice. Even if you do not want to become involved in management planning, they will help you to assess the present conservation value of a site, to decide what can be done to maintain or improve it, to choose good sites and species mixtures for the creation of new habitats, and to put these ideas into practice.

Attitudes to grasslands, heaths and moors

A very important aspect of management planning is to recognise the importance of the manager's preferences. Any plan that goes against the manager's natural inclinations will not be given the long-term commitment needed to put it into practice. If you are an adviser or consultant, understanding the prejudices, interests, likes and dislikes of your client(s) will be an important part of your job. Even if you are a land manager yourself, and more or less in control of the situation, you may need to give this some careful thought, for example before deciding how to react to advice you are given or how to respond to new grant opportunities to invest in conservation areas.

Those who are enthusiastic about grasslands, heaths and moors, whether from a conservation or commercial point of view, may be just as capable of doing damage through ill-considered action despite their good intentions as those who are indifferent about it.

Sowing an inappropriate seed mixture for the soil type or burning heather of the wrong age could both be damaging from a conservation point of view. Small changes to current practices, for instance in stocking regime, can also have a marked impact on plant and animal communities.

Positive guidelines

The important thing is to understand what you are doing and why, and to bear in mind the following simple guidelines:

▶ think before you act;

▶ first assess your area for its conservation and commercial value;

- draw up a management plan, however brief;
- monitor changes in the area, good and bad;
- be prepared to change your plans.

1.2   Types of grassland, heath and moor

Grasslands, heaths and moors may appear very different, but they do, in practice, have many factors in common. First, they are all open landscapes dominated by species of grasses or dwarf shrubs, with few or no trees. Secondly, they have nearly all been actively managed in some way over many centuries, needing frequent grazing, cutting or burning to maintain their existing characteristic vegetation. Thirdly, they are often areas of great beauty and, as a result, are of high recreational value. Lastly, they often contain sites of archaeological significance (in fact, some areas owe their continued existence as grassland to the presence of these sites).

Very little grassland, heath or moor is natural in Great Britain. Natural grassland only occurs where wind and low temperatures prevent tree growth, which is either on the coast or above the tree line (450–650 metres above sea level depending on the latitude). The original wildwood that covered much of the country has been cleared and prevented from regenerating by grazing, burning and cutting, largely implemented by farmers. Therefore, grasslands, heaths and moors can be viewed from two perspectives – the ecological one of semi-natural habitats and the agricultural one of productive grazing lands.

As there are two major perspectives in grassland management – the ecological and the agricultural – some terms may have different meanings for farmers or for conservationists, or the same feature may be described in different ways. You will need to understand these terms in order to follow properly any advice that you are given. Therefore, these and other useful terms are highlighted in bold type the first time that they appear in the text and they are also explained in the glossary (Appendix II). Furthermore, the common names of plant and animal species are used in the text but the scientific (Latin) names are given in Appendix III.

Semi-natural habitats

Grasslands, **heaths** and **moors** are classified into different habitat types mainly by the plant community present which in turn depends on the underlying rock, temperature and rainfall (which vary according to altitude and latitude).

Grasslands that are of conservation interest vary from **calcareous** grasslands which are rich in lime-loving plants through **neutral pastures** and hay **meadows** to **acidic** grasslands.   *Grasslands*

Chalk downland is found mainly in the south of Great Britain, but other types of calcareous grassland include the *limestone grasslands* of the Yorkshire Dales, the shell sands of the 'machair' which are found mainly in the Outer Hebrides, and some areas of alkaline (basic) soils, caused by wind and salt spray containing minerals such as calcium or magnesium, on the rocky west coast of Great Britain. There are also some recently created, artificial chalk habitats such as neglected chalk and limestone quarries, roadside verges and railway cuttings and embankments.

Neutral grasslands are found mainly on clay or **loam** soils and are used for grazing and/or hay production. There are several different types characterised by the water regime and the form of management which in turn combine with soil type and geographical location to influence the wildlife content of the habitat. There are potentially vast areas of neutral grasslands in Great Britain, but the majority have been drained, ploughed and re-seeded with a consequent reduction in their wildlife interest. Only 3% of old meadows remain unimproved.

Acidic grasslands are the most widespread type of **semi-natural** grassland in Great Britain. They occur on a great variety of soils from the free-draining acid sands of the Dorset heaths to the upland and montane soils of Scotland and Wales which can be either waterlogged peaty soils or relatively free-draining mineral soils. Correspondingly, the plant composition of these grasslands also varies widely. Unlike other grassland types, dwarf shrubs such as heather often grow in amongst the grasses to form what are known as *grass heaths*. These are the first part of a continuum which terminates in the true heaths dominated by heather.

Heaths

Heaths are dwarf scrub plant communities usually found in southern lowland Britain, often on porous sandy soils, cleared of woodland cover, where rainfall washes out the nutrients, leaving the soil impoverished and only able to support plants that are specially adapted to these conditions. Heaths are often dominated by species of heather, usually ling, and gorse but, if poorly managed, grasses, bracken and trees encroach. An arbitrary distinction is made between these lowland heaths and the upland heathlands or heather moorlands although the plant communities are different.

Moors

Moors occur mainly on the hard impervious rocks of the British uplands over 250 metres above sea level. These rocks release few nutrients to the soil and the strong winds, low temperatures and lack of sun, because of the greater cloud cover, restrict plant and animal growth. This results in low productivity and diversity, with certain **ericaceous** plants, or grasses, sedges and rushes, completely dominating the habitat. In the wettest and often lower-lying areas even tough grasses and heather cannot survive and **blanket bog** develops, producing a spongy covering of wet vegetation, mainly *Sphagnum* mosses. Moors fall into three broad categories that are fairly equal in extent: blanket bog moorland, heather moorland and grass moorland.

Scrub

All grazed lands are likely to change to a **scrub** or woodland habitat if unmanaged. Scrub has a wildlife value of its own and is often a feature of semi-natural grassland and heath habitats.

Productive grazing lands

Grass is the most important crop in Great Britain, accounting for two-thirds of the total area of crops and grass. In agricultural terms grasslands can be divided into two broad groups – the uncultivated or **unimproved grasslands** and the cultivated or **improved grasslands**. At the same time, while it is important to note that grazed grasslands are usually referred to as *pasture*, whereas grassland which is harvested for hay is called *meadow*, most meadows are also grazed at some times of the year.

Unimproved grasslands represent about 44% of the total area of grassland and consist of the following types.

Rough upland grazing

In *rough mountain and hill grazings* the plants are not of great agricultural value. They consist mainly of fescue, bent, mat and purple moor-grasses, as well as cotton grass, heather and gorse. Sheep and beef cattle can be supported only at very low stocking rates. Some areas are being afforested.

On *lowland heaths*, wavy hair-grass is very often the most common grass on the prevalent acid soils. These heaths occur in south and east England. Some of them have been reclaimed for grazing.

On the *downs of southern England* a wide range of herbs and grasses, such as sheep's fescue and upright brome, are found on the chalk and limestone soils.

The *fens in east and south-east England* are unreclaimed wetland areas, mostly poorly drained and dominated by plants such as purple moor-grass, rushes and sedges that are tolerant of periodically waterlogged ground conditions.

Improved grasslands have been managed to provide greater productivity through the use of drainage, fertilisers, pesticides or by sowing higher-yielding grass-seed mixtures. Improved grasslands represent 56% of the total area of grassland and include **permanent grassland** and **leys**.

Permanent grassland is grassland that is over five years old. It represents 41% of the total area of grassland as either pasture or meadows. As a group, permanent pastures cover a wide range, the nominal quality for grazing depending chiefly on the amount of perennial rye-grass in the **sward**. A first-grade permanent pasture contains more than 30% perennial rye-grass with a small amount of bent grasses; second-grade pasture has between 20% and 29% rye-grass and more bent grasses; and third-grade pasture tends to contain many more bent grasses with less than 20% rye-grass in the sward. Very poor permanent pastures are dominated by bent grasses, and on poorly drained soils most of the sward will be made up of bent grasses, rushes and sedges. Many permanent pastures can be readily improved for agricultural production.

Leys are temporary swards which have been sown with grass and clover for a limited period of up to five years. Leys represent about 15% of the total area of grassland. In most cases, depending on management, they will yield more than permanent grassland in their first years after sowing because of the more productive plants which make up the sward. But generally the sward will not stand up to trampling so well as permanent grassland and production is lost during the seedling phase.

As well as the largely agricultural areas of grassland, heath and moor, there are significant areas used mainly for amenity purposes. The area devoted to these uses is indicated in Table 1.1 (overleaf).

1.3   How to use this book

Readers of this book may be involved in managing many different types of grazed lands, from extensive areas of heather moorland to small grassy areas in the corners of arable fields. Your motivation could be a simple delight in the variety of wildlife that can be attracted to carefully planned and well managed areas or it could be a need to make as much money as possible from it, or a combination of the two. You may want to encourage game or create an attractive area for public recreation. Grasslands, heaths and moors can fulfil a wide variety of needs.

Table 1.1 Estimated proportion[1] of the land area of Great Britain[2] devoted to different categories of grasslands, heaths and moors

		%
Amenity grassland	Artificial, intensively managed areas[3]	1.7
	Semi-natural trampled open spaces[4]	1.8
	Semi-natural untrampled open spaces[5]	0.3
Rough grazings (common land)		5.4
Rough grazings (sole rights)[6]:		
	Blanket bog	6.5
	Heather moorland	7.4
	Grass moorland	6.3
	Lowland raised **mires**	0.4
	Lowland heath	0.2
	Chalk downland and limestone grassland	0.2
Permanent grassland[6]	Over 20 years old	9.8
	9–20 years old	4.9
	5–8 years old	4.9
Grass leys under 5 years old		<u>6.7</u>
		54.5

1 Note that because the figures are derived from several sources there is some overlap between categories.
2 Total land area of Great Britain is 22 million hectares.
3 Includes playing fields; golf fairways, greens and tees; domestic lawns; urban parks; urban and suburban road verges.
4 Includes common land with public access (but not all common rough grazings); golf rough; country parks; rural road verges; nature reserves.
5 Includes airports; railway and motorway embankments.
6 No separate figures are available for the area of herb-rich meadows.

General information on sources of advice and grants is given in the two supplementary booklets of the foundation module, *Helpful Organisations* and *Legislation and Regulations,* and will not be repeated here. Also, there is not enough space to go into much detail about commercial grassland management, but this subject is covered by several of the books listed in Appendix I. Both this book and the accompanying video cassette refer to the practical skills needed and the safety aspects of managing grazed lands, but there is no substitute for experience and you should, if necessary, attend a training course that will show you how to handle tools and machinery correctly.

The video cassette complements this book. Many aspects of conservation and management of grazed lands have an important visual element and are best conveyed by colour pictures. For example, wildlife assessment needs the ability to recognise the key species in an area, particularly plants. Landscape assessment takes a broader look at the area as a whole and the place of grasslands, heaths and moors within it. Many of the activities involved are best demonstrated by a moving picture. In Box 1.1 the contents of the video cassette and how they relate to this book are outlined. Throughout the book this margin flag indicates topics that are dealt with further in the video cassette.

If you work through this book from beginning to end, you will have a good understanding of grassland management in all its contexts. However, you may want to be more selective, to concentrate at one particular time on assessment or on implementation, or to cover only one particular type such as lowland heaths. To enable you to do this easily, Chapters 2, 3 and 4 deal with integrated assessment, Chapters 5 and 6 with management options for established and new areas respectively and Chapter 7 with implementation and the techniques used to fulfil the options. The examples used in this book illustrate the activities described and show you how to do them yourself. They are drawn chiefly from two case studies, one dealing with large-scale grassland and moorland in an upland area, and the other with smaller areas of grassland and heath on a lowland common. They are mainly in special case study sections at the end of each chapter and collectively give a complete picture of planning for practical conservation.

Each chapter also has an exercise for you to do, printed on a green background. These exercises are based on what you have read and should be done on an area to which you have legitimate access. The case study sections which follow these exercises will give you a wide enough range of examples to cover most of the situations you might choose.

1.4   The case studies

The following descriptions form the background to the two case studies.

Description of area

Borders hill farm

This farm of 991 hectares, having originally been two farms, occupies most of a secluded valley within the rolling Southern Uplands or Borders of Scotland.

The soil sequence is typical of the area, being in the main, the Linhope series of relatively free-draining, brown forest soils on the slopes, integrating with the Ettrick series of gleyed soils and, on the hill summits, an iron-pan podsol of the Minchmoor series and the impeded surface drainage of the Dod series. Occasional rocky outcrops occur further up the valley sides with alluvial deposits in the valley bottom. Rainfall is about 900 millimetres per year.

Varying in height from 150 to 530 metres, the majority of the land consists of rough hill grazings of heather moorland and acidic grasslands. On some of the steeper, and therefore more inaccessible slopes for machinery, are remnants of species-rich semi-natural grasslands of SSSI (Site of Special Scientific Interest) status. Only 106 hectares are enclosed of which 68 hectares are ploughable. The farm is tenanted and supports at present 1020 Blackface ewes and 40 Blue-Grey suckler cows.

There has been limited woodland planting for shelter on the farm itself. However, it is bounded on two sides by large-scale coniferous afforestation, planted over the last 35 years. Helping to soften the edge of the commercial forestry is a well-developed range of ancient semi-natural woodland of SSSI status, predominantly open to grazing by sheep and cattle.

Ownership

The farm has been in the ownership of the same family for three generations. The present owner has a low-key interest in the shooting on the farm, taking two or three days per year as a walk-up shoot. The lines of redundant grouse butts, however, are indicators of a healthier grouse population in the past.

Situated along one of the main old drove roads through Scotland this farming area is often mentioned in the tales and poems of Borders history, from battles with unwanted intruders to hunting expeditions by Scottish kings and noble-men. Today the visitors to the area are in pursuit of quieter rewards, as they follow the old drove road, now part of a national long-distance walk route.

Aims

The aims of both tenant and owner are to maintain the farm as a commercial hill sheep farm, possibly retaining some shooting although not as a commer-cial venture. The unique wildlife and conservation interests are to be accom-modated within the farming regime to ensure that they are maintained.

Stelling Minnis Common

Description of area

Area: 51 hectares

Designations: North Downs Area of Outstanding Natural Beauty; Kent Trust for Nature Conservation Site of Nature Conservation Interest (SNCI) on 2 hectares

Soil: Medium clay loam over clay-with-flints over chalk; shallow patches of brick-earth soils in places

Ownership and other interests

The owners are the Trustees of the Estate of the late Lord Tomlin who held the title of 'Lord of the Manor'.

Stelling Minnis Common is one of the last remaining manorial commons in Kent with 46 rights of common. The main groups interested in the common are:

▶ the Conservators (appointed by the Trustees, responsible for day-to-day management);

▶ The Commoners' Association (looks after the interests of registered commoners);

▶ The Friends of Stelling Minnis (raises funds to enable the Conservators to do the work).

The Common also has considerable public and recreational use, both by local residents and by visitors. There is free access and car parking.

Wildlife interest

Stelling Minnis Common is of considerable wildlife as well as landscape and amenity value. The main wildlife interest centres on the remaining unimproved acidic grasslands, on which fragments of lowland heath vegetation survive.

Although bracken and scrub are encroaching, clumps of mature scrub and secondary woodland add to the habitat for e.g. birds. Mowing maintains the open grass areas, but tends to make them rather uniform.

Summary

It is an area of considerable interest, historically, ecologically and for its land-scape and amenity value. It is intriguing, not least for its need to maintain a balance between the various interest groups: the access, residential and conser-vation objectives of these groups are all valid but sometimes conflicting.

Chapter 2
LANDSCAPE ASSESSMENT

Great Britain has long been described as a 'green and pleasant land'. Much of that impression is caused by the amount of grassland in the countryside, and how it remains green throughout all but the driest summers and yet provides points of colour in the spring and subtle changes in tone in the winter. Equally, this country is renowned for its purple heather-clad upland scenery and its sandy lowland heaths. Such areas are greatly valued because of the sights, smells and sounds they convey while their scale and low level of human occupation provide a 'wilderness' to walk, relax and reflect in, away from the rigours of modern life.

Not all grazed areas are large, however, and the patchwork quilt of permanent grass, leys, bare ground, wheat, oilseed rape and other crops in lowland areas or valley bottoms are also distinctive landscape features. Indeed, grasslands, heaths and moors are a major provider of colour in the countryside, filling in the areas between buildings, roads, walls, hedgerows and woodlands, and cloaking the hills and mountains. All land managers, and in particular farmers, are in a position to influence this colour in the landscape through their management activities. Past management activities have been instrumental in shaping the countryside we see today so planning future activities properly is important, and the effects of all these activities can be better understood through a landscape assessment.

2.1   Historical origins

Woodland was the natural vegetation cover of much of Great Britain after the last glaciation until humans started to clear it for rearing stock, growing crops, and to provide wood for fuel and timber around 3500 BC. Natural grassland was largely confined to high altitudes and to very infertile soils. The open habitats of grassland, heath and moor, therefore, owe their existence to the progressive felling and clearance of the original wildwood but, secondly, and more importantly, to the continued effects of grazing, felling and burning. Any area of vegetation that is treated like grassland, by regular grazing, cutting and burning, will eventually become a grassland. This is because grasses can withstand regular removal of their leaves while many other plants cannot. The ability to regenerate from the base of the plant gives grasses a competitive advantage under continuous pressure from grazing, cutting and burning. This is also true to a certain extent of shrubby heather plants on heaths and moors under light grazing, although they also owe their existence to particular soil conditions (heavy grazing kills heather and allows grasses to take over).

The actual history of a site or area can be quite varied. It may have been under grass, cultivation and trees at several different times as the climate and the economy changed. Many lowland heaths and upland moors formerly supported large settlements and were under cultivation for many years. Some areas have been mainly grazed by cattle, others by sheep for several centuries, and yet others only in the past 200 years. In recent history grazing by rabbits has also had a considerable impact on chalk and sandy soils (although introduced by the Normans, rabbits have only thrived outside captivity since the 18th century). In addition, our ability to cut grasslands for hay has gradually improved as first hand scythes, then horse-drawn mowers and finally motorised harvesters were introduced. In every case the vegetation of the open habitats has had to adapt. Lastly, fires have often been a 'natural' feature of lowland heaths while burning has been used as a specific management technique to create the right conditions for heather moors to support grouse for shooting, a pastime dependent on the development of appropriate firearms.

2.2   *General landscape assessment*

Landscape assessment in general involves gaining an overall impression of the land and of how the details fit together to make up the whole picture. This will depend on the variation, from one area to another, in:

- ▶ the landform (the underlying skeleton of rocks and soil);
- ▶ the covering of vegetation;
- ▶ the buildings and historical and archaeological features (structures);
- ▶ the cultural associations of the area concerned;
- ▶ the human needs that it fulfils.

General landscape assessment is described in the foundation book. It involves selecting several viewpoints to give a complete coverage of the area you are interested in; marking these on a map of the area and filling in a checklist for each viewpoint; and recording your impressions formally using notes, photographs, sketches and maps (not forgetting to consider your personal preferences and perceptions and the needs and desires of other people who may have an interest in the area). It is important to keep systematic records and, if appropriate, to divide up the holding into clearly recognisable zones for separate assessment to provide a basis for the long-term management of the land.

A more detailed assessment, which concentrates on the existing grassland, heath and moor, should focus particularly on:

- ▶ the shape of the grassland, heath or moor;
- ▶ the scale of the grassland, heath or moor;
- ▶ the diversity of the area in colour and plant species composition;
- ▶ the presence of any features of archaeological interest;
- ▶ footpaths and public viewpoints.

In assessing the landscape of an area, personal preferences and fashion are involved to some extent. However, there are a few widely accepted rules to guide you, at least until you have the self-confidence and experience to develop your own assessment methods. Note how important it is to consider the areas of grass in relation to the surrounding landscape

Shape and scale of the area

The shape of an area of grassland, heath or moor is determined by its boundaries and the topography of the underlying land. Much attention to shape will reflect whether these boundaries are straight and distinct or irregular and blurred. Grazed fields are often clearly delineated by hedges, walls or roads, with a more or less uniform colour and rectangular shape, while heaths and moors are often more open with a greater likelihood of scrub or trees being present to break up the colour and 'texture' of the scenery. Although the latter have a more 'natural' appearance, enclosed fields are a prominent feature of our natural heritage and both can sit side by side in an appropriate setting. Grassland is also an important feature of the built environment whether as village greens, playing fields, parks or gardens. Their ubiquitous nature makes them a key landscape feature.

When assessing the scale of an area the viewpoints chosen will be very important and should concentrate on the most frequented or more easily accessible sites. Generally speaking, a larger-scale landscape is one with wide areas of land visible for a considerable distance, which is often the case with upland moorland. In smaller-scale landscapes the views are shorter and more restricted, and distinctive features are closer together. Similarly, there are marked differences between the rolling hills of downland areas, flat hay meadows, and the craggy hills and rock outcrops of upland moorland.

Diversity of landscape features

The various types of grasslands, heaths and moors provide a wide range of colours and 'textures' in the landscape that change from season to season. For instance, the green of a hay meadow in winter can become spotted with the yellows, whites and pinks of flowers in the spring and early summer, turn a dramatically yellowy-brown when cut and gradually turn green again as the grass regrows. Similarly the dusty green of heaths, interspersed with light, sandy patches and clumps of darker green gorse bushes early in the year, becomes a carpet of purple heather flowers with bright yellow patches of flowering gorse in later months.

The greater uniformity of colour of improved grasslands detracts from the smaller-scale landscape within one or two fields, but the larger-scale landscape can still be appealing where there is a variety of of colours present through grazed, cropped and bare fields. And the colours of this patchwork of enclosed fields also change from year to year as the cropping pattern changes, unlike the more permanent open areas of unimproved grassland, heath and moor.

Archaeological features

The extent of grasslands, heaths and moors, and their artificial origins, make them particularly rich in ancient monuments and other archaeological remains. Many archaeological sites can easily be recognised by the presence of ruins, upstanding stone structures, banks, ditches, mounds, hollows, or uneven ground.

Other sites, of equal importance, are totally buried and therefore almost invisible at ground level. These are more difficult to find and often only come to light by chance when the ground is disturbed, or during special types of archaeological survey such as field-walking or aerial reconnaissance. Dark patches in a ploughed field, scattered pottery or flint, stony areas, or changes in vegetation may, however, provide clues to the existence of a buried site.

Earthworks

Because grass has shallow roots and **turf** has a tough surface, pasture, especially when grazed by sheep, provides the ideal covering for ancient monuments, particularly **earthworks**. Earthworks under pasture can often be seen best when the sun is low in the sky and casts long shadows.

Also preserved beneath pasture are abandoned prehistoric and medieval fields, for example strip **lynchets** and **ridge and furrow**, and monuments such as deserted villages, hill forts, Roman camps, old tracks, rabbit warrens, boundary dykes, and castles. Ritual sites such as burial mounds (barrows) and sacred enclosures (henges) also survive well under pasture.

Some of these archaeological sites will be designated but many have no special status. However, their value as part of our landscape and cultural heritage is as significant as listed buildings and all efforts should be made not to damage them.

As long as monuments are under pasture they are best managed by using the land for light grazing. Otherwise, few special management measures are necessary beyond the prevention of soil erosion by livestock or the colonization of the site by burrowing animals.

Lowland heaths

The archaeological remains in lowland heaths fall into two groups: monuments relating to the period before the heath formed, and those forming part of the exploitation of the heath itself. Many of them are earthworks because subsequent land use has not destroyed them. The richness of the remains found in heaths shows how important such areas were as areas to live and farm until disturbance of the original vegetation and the fragile soils, mostly in prehistoric times, produced the heaths we see today.

Traditional heathland management based on low density grazing is ideal for preserving monuments. Bracken needs to be controlled because of its deeply penetrating root systems, and tree growth on ancient monuments should be prevented. Erosion by animals and visitors also needs to be kept in check.

Upland moors

Upland moors were not always the desolate rugged landscapes we see today. During periods when the climate was warmer than it is now they were heavily occupied and the land was used for cultivation and grazing. Because stone was the main building material used in the uplands, much of the evidence of these episodes of exploitation is still visible above ground level.

Barrows, enclosures, settlements, hut circles, standing stones, **cairns**, stone circles, stone rows, hill forts, field systems, quarries and mines represent the variety of activities practised at different times.

Traditional management of moorland is compatible with preserving archaeological sites as long as the land is not overexploited. In particular, it is important to maintain the fragile vegetation cover by controlling erosion by stock and visitors.

The public interest

The person who owns or manages a piece of land inevitably sees it differently to outsiders. Any landscape assessment should take account of both points of view – those of the manager of the land and those members of the public who may drive past it, walk though it or view it from a distance.

This is particularly the case with grazed lands because they make up so much of the countryside and are a positive source of amenity and recreation for many people. Equally, many sites, such as country parks and golf courses, are managed with amenity and recreation as the main objectives and so a balance is needed between conservation and other land uses. In some important landscape areas a public interest has been formally declared by their designation as National Parks, Areas of Outstanding Natural Beauty (AONBs) in England and Wales or National Scenic Areas (NSAs) in Scotland, or Environmentally Sensitive Areas (ESAs) throughout Great Britain (see the *Legislation and Regulations* booklet of the foundation module for further details).

2.3 Making your own landscape assessment of grassland, heath or moor

In the previous section the features of landscape assessment are described, but the only way to learn more is to do it for yourself.

As suggested in Chapter 1, choose an area of grassland, heath or moor to which you have legitimate access and make a landscape assessment of it. Remember that, ideally, you should first assess the place of all the vegetation types in the landscape as a whole, as described in the foundation book and summarised briefly here, before going on to assess the individual grassland, heath or moor areas themselves. At this stage you should use maps to mark viewpoints and significant features, and photographs, sketches and checklists to record the *present* state of the landscape as a basis for planning changes and as a reference point against which to measure the effects of these changes. You may also want to seek out historical documents, maps and photographs to provide information on the *past* state of the landscape for comparison.

General landscape assessment

1   Draw a sketch map of your area (or use an Ordnance Survey map) and mark prominent features inside and outside it. Annotate the map with comments on these features and mark any distinct landscape zones.

2   Draw sketches or take photographs showing distant views of the area. Mark each viewpoint on your map. Include any viewpoints that are important to the general public, for example views of fields from main roads or villages, as well as those of personal interest to the land owner or manager. Attach for each photograph or sketch a note describing:

▶   the viewpoint from which it was taken;

▶   the reason for choosing that viewpoint, particularly noting anything of public interest;

▶   the shape of the grassland, heath or moor areas;

▶   the scale of the grassland, heath or moor areas;

▶   your personal perceptions.

Grassland, heath or moor landscape assessment

(Note that these guidelines are for existing grassland, heath and moor. Where new habitats are being considered the assessment should be based on a full general management planning exercise, as summarised in Section 1.1.)

1   Draw a sketch map of the grassland, heath or moor area, marking any distinctive landscape features. Draw close-up sketches or take photographs of the areas, including views from outside and from inside, particularly of notable features such as ponds. Identify any areas with particularly interesting characteristics such as old ridges. As in (2) above, for each sketch or photograph mark the viewpoint on your map and add notes describing:

•   the viewpoint from which it was taken;

> the reason for choosing the viewpoint, particularly noting anything of public interest;

> the diversity of the habitat and the colours shown;

> historical and archaeological features;

> your personal perceptions.

2   Record any restrictions or designations relevant to the role of the grassland, heath or moor in the landscape or to the treatment of individual sites:

> National Parks (in England and Wales);

> AONBs (in England and Wales);

> NSAs (in Scotland);

> Environmentally Sensitive Areas;

> public access, footpaths, bridleways;

> ancient monuments;

> common land.

2.4   Landscape assessment of case study areas

The following examples of landscape assessment, based on the two case studies described at the end of Chapter 1, will give you some guidance on what to do. They are not rigid templates, indeed they incorporate the personal views of the assessor. You will develop your own methods as you become more experienced.

Borders hill farm

The farm occupies one of the numerous valleys which dissects the picturesque Southern Uplands or Borders. Apparently unremarkable from adjoining hill farms with its rough grazing land, the interesting mix of habitats can be appreciated only as you enter the small glen.

Viewpoint 1

Driving up the narrow windy road in viewpoint 1, you feel drawn into a place of sanctuary (see Figure 2.1). In the summer the steep bankings, yellow with rock-rose flowers, and the air busy with insect life is a picture of colourful relaxation. In the autumn the deciduous woodland fringe and scattered bracken cover offer a range of more subdued and subtle colours. Winter reasserts the glen as a safe haven from the blizzards of the hill tops. The landscape features are summarised in Table 2.1 (overleaf), using the checklist in Section 2.3 of the foundation book.

Viewpoint 2

In contrast to the calm secure valley there is a more open, wild landscape on the hill tops (see Figure 2.2). Viewpoint 2 follows into the distance the rows of undulating hills along the northern edge of the Borders. Their irregular patchwork of heather, grass and evergreen shelter plantings appear more muted in colour. From this vantage point the range of habitats on the case study farm can be viewed with ease. In the summer there are contrasting greens of improved pasture, rough grazings and deciduous woodland which become more subtle with the turning of autumn. In the winter, the hill tops would be a bleak haunt, only for the experienced walker. Table 2.2 (overleaf) shows the landscape perception for this viewpoint, as suggested in Section 2.3 of the foundation book.

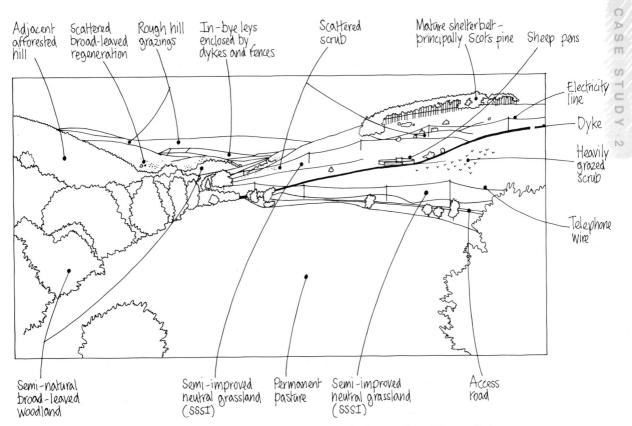

Figure 2.1 labels:

Adjacent afforested hill

Scattered broad-leaved regeneration

Rough hill grazings

In-bye leys enclosed by dykes and fences

Scattered scrub

Mature shelterbelt – principally Scots pine

Sheep pens

Electricity line

Dyke

Heavily grazed scrub

Telephone wire

Semi-natural broad-leaved woodland

Semi-improved neutral grassland (SSSI)

Permanent pasture

Semi-improved neutral grassland (SSSI)

Access road

Figure 2.1   The landscape from viewpoint 1, the access track to the farm only, with tantalizing views of the hill tops

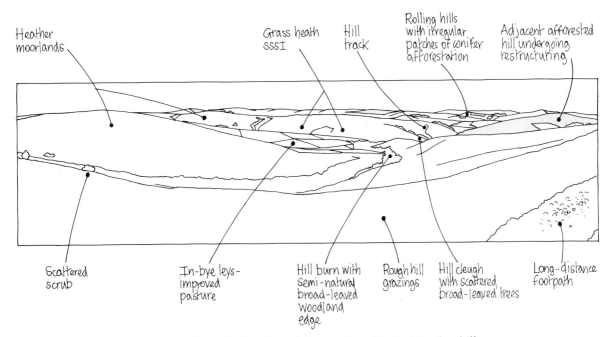

Figure 2.2 labels:

Heather moorlands

Grass heath SSSI

Hill track

Rolling hills with irregular patches of conifer afforestation

Adjacent afforested hill undergoing restructuring

Scattered scrub

In-bye leys – improved pasture

Hill burn with semi-natural broad-leaved woodland edge

Rough hill grazings

Hill cleugh with scattered broad-leaved trees

Long-distance footpath

Figure 2.2   The landscape from viewpoint 2, a long-distance view of typical Borders hill-farming landscape, as seen from the long-distance path

Table 2.1 Checklist of landscape features: landform, vegetation and structures

Grade the relative contribution of each feature as follows: *inconspicuous;
**noticeable; ***conspicuous.

Land holding Borders Hill Farm   Viewpoint number I

Date September 1991   Time of day 3·10 Mid afternoon

Weather Sunny, slight cloud, clear

Landform

Plain	Coast	Marsh	Lake
Lowland **	Estuary	Mudflat	Pond
Plateau	Broad valley	Dune	River
Hill ***	Narrow valley ***	Beach	Stream **
Crag or cliff	Deep gorge		Canal
Mountain			Ditch

Slopes

Vertical	Steep	(Gently sloping)
(Undulating)	Flat	

Vegetation

Woodland

Broad-leaved woodland ***	Mixed woodland
Coniferous woodland ***	Scrub **

Heathland and grassland

Heather moorland **	Bracken **
Upland grass moor ***	Lowland heath
Peat bog	Lowland unimproved grassland
Water meadow	

Cultivated land

Arable land	Market gardens and orchards
Improved pasture **	Parkland

Linear features

Hedgerows	Roadside verges *
Woodland fringe ***	Railway embankments
River banks ***	

Small isolated features

Isolated trees	Small shelter-belts ***
Groups of trees, mainly broad-leaved (less than 0.25 ha)	Copses and spinneys
Groups of trees, mainly coniferous (less than 0.25 ha)	Small gardens

Structures

Buildings	Fences
Farmyards	Walls *** ** Dykes
Camp sites	Telephone wires **
Car parks	Electricity pylons *
Quarries	Rubbish dumps
Industrial land	Derelict land

Table 2.2 Landscape perception of the Borders hill farm

Criterion	Suggested descriptions*
Scale	Intimate, small, (large) vast
Enclosure	Tight, enclosed, (open) (exposed)
Variety/diversity	Uniform, simple, (varied) (complex) surprising
Harmony	Well balanced, (harmonious,) discordant, chaotic
Movement	Dead, (calm,) lively, busy, frantic
Texture	Smooth, (rough,) coarse-grained
Naturalness	(Wild,) unmanaged, remote, undisturbed
Tidiness	(Untidy,) neat, over-managed (jumble)
Colour	Monochrome, (subtle) (muted,) colourful, garish
Smell	(Pleasant) unpleasant, obnoxious
Sound	Intrusive, noisy, (quiet)
Rarity	Ordinary, unusual, rare, unique, (familiar)
Security	(Comfortable) safe, intimate, unsettling, threatening
Stimulus	Boring, monotonous, bland, (interesting,) surprising, (invigorating)
Beauty	Ugly, uninspiring, pretty, (attractive,) majestic, (picturesque)

depending on weather!

(Source: Adapted from Countryside Commission, 1987)

*The lists in this column are not intended to imply a scale of values from good to bad; the words are not arranged in any particular order.

General landscape assessment

The image of the Southern Uplands has long been associated with such an exposed rough landscape – the sign of a truly 'natural' wild countryside to many people. For others, it is an impoverished environment, the result of thousands of years of human influence. Sir Walter Scott, the 18th century Scottish romantic novelist, and local sheriff, lived for a time near to the case study farm. He was familiar with the local landscape and its pastimes, and his poem 'Marmion' comments on this question of its 'naturalness'. There is no doubting his views on the demise of the great hunting forest and its associated pursuits.

'The scenes are desert now, and bare,
Where flourished once a forest fair,
When these waste glens with copse were lined,
And peopled with that hart and hind…

While doe and roe and red-deer good,
Have bounded by through gay green-wood…

A thousand vassals mustered round,
With horse, and hawk, and horn, and hound;
And I might see the youth intent
Guard every pass with cross-bow bent;
And through the brake the rangers stalk,
And falc'ners hold the ready hawk;
And foresters, in green-wood trim,
Lead in the leash the graze-hounds grim…'

21

To many of the walkers who visit the area, the attraction is undoubtedly the open views and the battle against the elements. To the drovers of days past this route would have been have preferable to the lower, wetter valley bottoms, filled with thick scrub and a potential haven for bands of thieves. An earthwork, comprising a ditch and a bank, may have been constructed at this or an earlier time to deter attacks or simply to control movement of traffic along the drove road.

Stelling Minnis Common

North Downs AONB and Kent County Council Special Landscape Area

Geology: on the North Downs plateau, where the chalk is overlain with clay-with-flints

Topography: 140–145 metres above sea level, flat or very slightly undulating

Climate: rainfall average 600–800 millimetres per year (NB: no streams, but one or two ponds)

History

Stelling Minnis Common was recorded in the Domesday Book as part of the possessions of Odo, half-brother of William.

One of the few remaining unenclosed and little altered remnants of the medieval manors, the 'Lord's Waste' of the Manor of Stelling.

Rights to the 'waste' included to graze a cow, goat, sheep or pig and to collect firewood, forage and bedding (bracken and gorse) and material for roofing.

Small areas of land were gradually enclosed from the waste, legally or illegally, and those who were not driven away passed these smallholdings to their descendants, who grazed their cattle and sheep on the Common. These became the Commoners' Rights, and were confirmed under the Commons Registration Act of 1965.

Decline of grazing

A large and important heath in the 19th century, Stelling Minnis Common was still grazed by commoners' animals until a few years after the First World War.

Gated at this time, the advent of the motor car made gates less popular and they fell into disuse. New house-owners have had less interest in the traditional open landscape of the Common, and more interest in it as somewhere generally pleasant to live.

Present landscape

Today, Stelling Minnis Common can be divided into roughly three areas (see Figure 2.3). (This is somewhat arbitrary, as scrub, trees and pockets of woodland are scattered throughout.)

General landscape assessment

The houses are well-dispersed among the trees and scrub, and the area feels very rural even close to the houses. The viewpoint in Figure 2.4 and the checklists in Tables 2.3 and 2.4 (overleaf) are looking towards the houses.

Most visitors who come by car go to the central, open part of the common. Many stay close to their cars. Other users are horse-riders, walkers and cyclists. On the whole the recreational users are well-absorbed by the natural screening of trees and scrub.

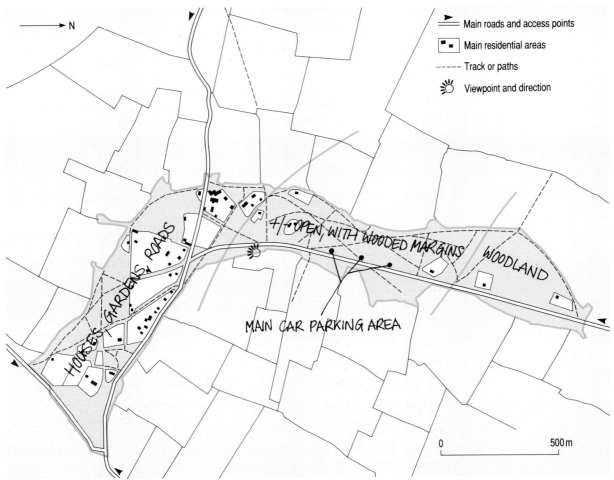

Legend:
- Main roads and access points
- Main residential areas
- Track or paths
- Viewpoint and direction

N

+/- OPEN, WITH WOODED MARGINS

WOODLAND

HOUSES GARDENS ROADS

MAIN CAR PARKING AREA

0   500 m

Figure 2.3   Landscape assessment map of Stelling Minnis Common

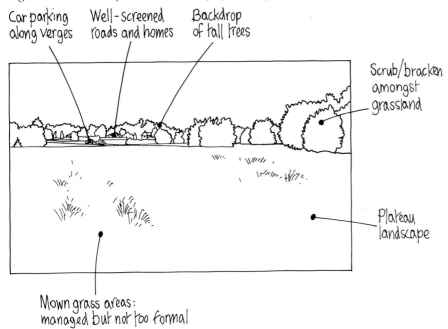

Car parking along verges

Well-screened roads and homes

Backdrop of tall trees

Scrub/bracken amongst grassland

Plateau landscape

Mown grass areas: managed but not too formal

Figure 2.4   Annotated sketch of Stelling Minnis Common from the viewpoint marked on Figure 2.3

Table 2.3 Checklist of landscape features: landform, vegetation and structures

Grade the relative contribution of each feature as follows: *inconspicuous;
**noticeable; ***conspicuous.

Land holding Stelling Minnis Common ......   Viewpoint number I

Date 15.8.91   Time of day   1 p.m.

Weather Fine, sunny

Landform

Plain	Coast	Marsh	Lake
Lowland *	Estuary	Mudflat	Pond *
Plateau **	Broad valley	Dune	River
Hill	Narrow valley	Beach	Stream
Crag or cliff	Deep gorge		Canal
Mountain			Ditch

Slopes

Vertical	Steep	Gently sloping
Undulating	(Flat)	

Vegetation

Woodland

Broad-leaved woodland **	Mixed woodland *
Coniferous woodland	Scrub ***

Heathland and grassland

Heather moorland	Bracken **
Upland grass moor	Lowland heath ***
Peat bog	Lowland unimproved grassland **
Water meadow	

Cultivated land

Arable land	Market gardens and orchards
Improved pasture	Parkland

Linear features

Hedgerows **	Roadside verges **
Woodland fringe ***	Railway embankments
River banks	

Small isolated features

Isolated trees **	Small shelter-belts
Groups of trees, mainly broad-leaved (less than 0.25 ha) ***	Copses and spinneys
Groups of trees, mainly coniferous (less than 0.25 ha)	Small gardens **

Structures

Buildings ***	Fences *
Farmyards	Walls
Camp sites	Telephone wires **
Car parks	Electricity pylons
Quarries **	Rubbish dumps
Industrial land	Derelict land

Table 2.4   Landscape perception of Stelling Minnis Common

Criterion	Suggested descriptions*
Scale	Intimate, (small) large, vast
Enclosure	Tight, (enclosed) open, exposed
Variety/diversity	Uniform, simple, varied (complex) surprising
Harmony	Well balanced (harmonious) discordant, chaotic
Movement	Dead, calm, (lively) busy, frantic
Texture	Smooth, rough, (coarse-grained)
Naturalness	Wild, unmanaged, remote, (undisturbed)
Tidiness	Untidy, (neat,) over-managed
Colour	Monochrome, subtle, (muted,) colourful, garish
Smell	(Pleasant,) unpleasant, obnoxious
Sound	Intrusive, noisy, (quiet)
Rarity	Ordinary, (unusual,) rare, unique, familiar
Security	Comfortable, (safe,) intimate, unsettling, threatening
Stimulus	Boring, monotonous, bland, (interesting,) surprising, invigorating
Beauty	Ugly, uninspiring, pretty, attractive, majestic, (picturesque)

(Source: Adapted from Countryside Commission, 1987)

*The lists in this column are not intended to imply a scale of values from good to bad; the words are not arranged in any particular order.

HE SAYS THE LANDSCAPE CERTAINLY LOOKS DIFFERENT FROM DOWN HERE!

HABITAT ASSESSMENT

Habitat assessment, as described in Chapter 3 of the foundation book, requires at least some understanding of the relationships between the living and non-living aspects of an area. It is useful to be able to name the plants and animals that you find in a habitat, to understand why they might be there and how they are likely to react to changes in the habitat, and to recognise the signs that indicate an area may be particularly valuable from a wildlife point of view. The interactions between physical and ecological processes shape a habitat, and any management measures have to work with, rather than against, them. This chapter describes how to assess the wildlife value of a site using the assessment criteria of naturalness, diversity, rarity and size; criteria that will help you plan appropriate conservation measures to maintain, enhance, or even create, valued grassland, heath or moor.

3.1   Grassland, heath and moor ecosystems

Grazed land in Great Britain may often appear superficially to be uniform because of the green colouring, but this colour hides an extremely wide range of plant and animal communities. Soil type, climate and topography are all very important factors in shaping those communities as they determine the range and diversity of the plant and animal species. The way in which those species interact with each other and their environment are equally important, especially when these interactions or ecological processes have occurred over many years and over a large area. Many of these interactions are summarised in Figures 3.1, 3.2 and 3.3 for the three main categories of grazed land: lowland grassland, lowland heath and upland moor. The arrows indicate the flow of energy and/or organic material within the various communities and the thickness of the arrows indicates the extent of their influence on the ecosystem.

Physical factors

The major factors controlling the distribution of species, and through them habitats, are soil type, climate, topography, and human interference (which is covered later). The effects of soil type, climate and topography cannot always be separated as the soil type itself depends partly on such factors as rainfall and temperature, which in turn are influenced by topography.

Soils

Soil type is determined by rainfall, drainage and the type of rock from which it has been formed. Soil formed from calcareous rocks is rich in calcium (lime) and therefore **alkaline** but that formed from **siliceous** rock is acidic because of the lack of calcium. Great Britain's rocks are predominantly siliceous in the north and west, and calcareous in the south and east.

Rain removes calcium as it drains through the soil; because the rainfall is four to five times greater in the west than in the east, the contrast between the acidic soils of the north and west and the alkaline soils of the south and east becomes even sharper. Leaching by rainfall can also remove other

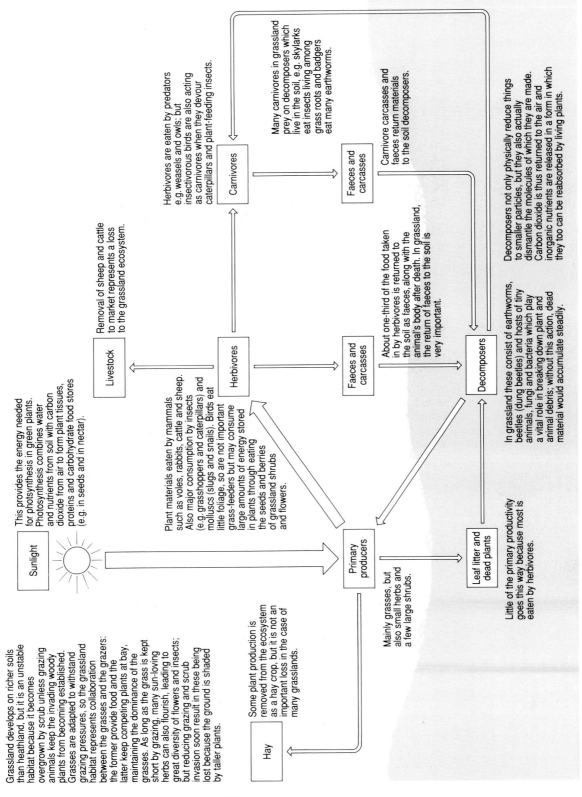

Figure 3.1   The lowland grassland ecosystem. (After Morris, 1980)

Grassland develops on richer soils than heathland, but it is an unstable habitat because it becomes overgrown by scrub unless grazing animals keep the invading woody plants from becoming established. Grasses are adapted to withstand grazing pressures, so the grassland habitat represents collaboration between the grasses and the grazers: the former provide food and the latter keep competing plants at bay, maintaining the dominance of the grasses. As long as the grass is kept short by grazing, many sun-loving herbs can also flourish, leading to great diversity of flowers and insects; but reducing grazing and scrub invasion soon result in these being lost because the ground is shaded by taller plants.

Some plant production is removed from the ecosystem as a hay crop, but it is not an important loss in the case of many grasslands.

Hay

Sunlight

This provides the energy needed for photosynthesis in green plants. Photosynthesis combines water and nutrients from soil with carbon dioxide from air to form plant tissues, proteins and carbohydrate food stores (e.g. in seeds and in nectar).

Removal of sheep and cattle to market represents a loss to the grassland ecosystem.

Livestock

Herbivores are eaten by predators e.g. weasels and owls; but insectivorous birds are also acting as carnivores when they devour caterpillars and plant-feeding insects.

Many carnivores in grassland prey on decomposers which live in the soil, e.g. skylarks eat insects living among grass roots and badgers eat many earthworms.

Carnivores

Carnivore carcasses and faeces return materials to the soil decomposers.

Faeces and carcasses

Plant materials eaten by mammals such as voles, rabbits, cattle and sheep. Also major consumption by insects (e.g. grasshoppers and caterpillars) and molluscs (slugs and snails). Birds eat little foliage, so are not important grass-feeders but may consume large amounts of energy stored in plants through eating the seeds and berries of grassland shrubs and flowers.

Herbivores

About one-third of the food taken in by herbivores is returned to the soil as faeces, along with the animal's body after death. In grassland, the return of faeces to the soil is very important.

Faeces and carcasses

Decomposers not only physically reduce things to smaller particles, but they also actually dismantle the molecules of which they are made. Carbon dioxide is thus returned to the air and inorganic nutrients are released in a form which they too can be reabsorbed by living plants.

Primary producers

Mainly grasses, but also small herbs and a few large shrubs.

Leaf litter and dead plants

Little of the primary productivity goes this way because most is eaten by herbivores.

Decomposers

In grassland these consist of earthworms, beetles (dung beetles) and hosts of tiny animals, fungi and bacteria which play a vital role in breaking down plant and animal debris; without this action, dead material would accumulate steadily.

27

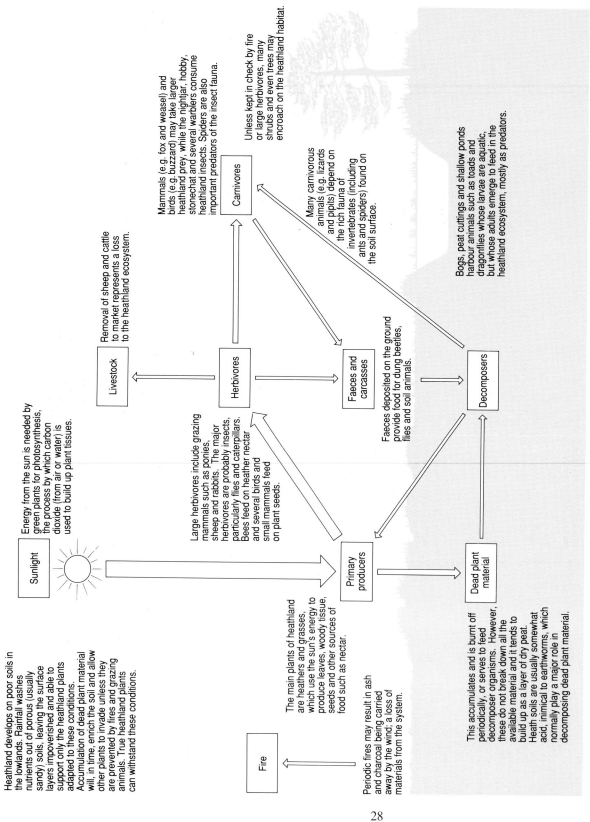

Figure 3.2   The lowland heath ecosystem. (After Morris, 1980)

Heathland develops on poor soils in the lowlands. Rainfall washes nutrients out of porous (usually sandy) soils, leaving the surface layers impoverished and able to support only the heathland plants adapted to these conditions. Accumulation of dead plant material will, in time, enrich the soil and allow other plants to invade unless they are prevented by fires and grazing animals. True heathland plants can withstand these conditions.

The main plants of heathland are heathers and grasses, which use the sun's energy to produce leaves, woody tissue, seeds and other sources of food such as nectar.

Periodic fires may result in ash and charcoal being carried away by the wind; a loss of materials from the system.

This accumulates and is burnt off periodically, or serves to feed decomposer organisms. However, these do not break down all the available material and it tends to build up as a layer of dry peat. Heath soils are usually somewhat acid, inimical to earthworms, which normally play a major role in decomposing dead plant material.

Energy from the sun is needed by green plants for photosynthesis, the process by which carbon dioxide (from air or water) is used to build up plant tissues.

Large herbivores include grazing mammals such as ponies, sheep and rabbits. The major herbivores are probably insects, particularly flies and caterpillars. Bees feed on heather nectar and several birds and small mammals feed on plant seeds.

Removal of sheep and cattle to market represents a loss to the heathland ecosystem.

Faeces deposited on the ground provide food for dung beetles, flies and soil animals.

Mammals (e.g. fox and weasel) and birds (e.g. buzzard) may take larger heathland prey, while the nightjar, hobby, stonechat and several warblers consume heathland insects. Spiders are also important predators of the insect fauna.

Many carnivorous animals (e.g. lizards and pipits) depend on the rich fauna of invertebrates (including ants and spiders) found on the soil surface.

Unless kept in check by fire or large herbivores, many shrubs and even trees may encroach on the heathland habitat.

Bogs, peat cuttings and shallow ponds harbour animals such as toads and dragonflies whose larvae are aquatic, but whose adults emerge to feed in the heathland ecosystem, mostly as predators.

Fire

Sunlight

Primary producers

Dead plant material

Livestock

Herbivores

Faeces and carcasses

Decomposers

Carnivores

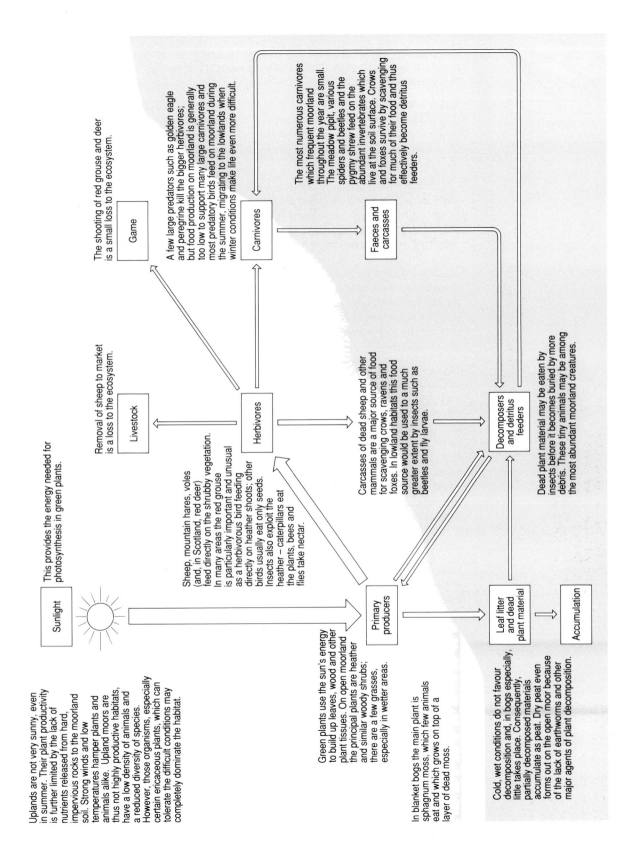

Uplands are not very sunny, even in summer. Their plant productivity is further limited by the lack of nutrients released from hard, impervious rocks to the moorland soil. Strong winds and low temperatures hamper plants and animals alike. Upland moors are thus not highly productive habitats, have a low density of animals and a reduced diversity of species.
However, those organisms, especially certain ericaceous plants, which can tolerate the difficult conditions may completely dominate the habitat.

This provides the energy needed for photosynthesis in green plants.

Sunlight

Removal of sheep to market is a loss to the ecosystem.

Livestock

The shooting of red grouse and deer is a small loss to the ecosystem.

Game

A few large predators such as golden eagle and peregrine kill the bigger herbivores; but food production on moorland is generally too low to support many large carnivores and most predatory birds feed on moorland during the summer, migrating to the lowlands when winter conditions make life even more difficult.

Herbivores

Sheep, mountain hares, voles (and, in Scotland, red deer) feed directly on the shrubby vegetation. In many areas the red grouse is particularly important and unusual as a herbivorous bird feeding directly on heather shoots; other birds usually eat only seeds. Insects also exploit the heather – caterpillars eat the plants, bees and flies take nectar.

Carnivores

The most numerous carnivores which frequent moorland throughout the year are small. The meadow pipit, various spiders and beetles and the pygmy shrew feed on the abundant invertebrates which live at the soil surface. Crows and foxes survive by scavenging for much of their food and thus effectively become detritus feeders.

Faeces and carcasses

Carcasses of dead sheep and other mammals are a major source of food for scavenging crows, ravens and foxes. In lowland habitats this food source would be used to a much greater extent by insects such as beetles and fly larvae.

Decomposers and detritus feeders

Dead plant material may be eaten by insects before it becomes buried by more debris. These tiny animals may be among the most abundant moorland creatures.

Primary producers

Green plants use the sun's energy to build up leaves, wood and other plant tissues. On open moorland the principal plants are heather and similar woody shrubs; there are a few grasses, especially in wetter areas.

In blanket bogs the main plant is sphagnum moss, which few animals eat and which grows on top of a layer of dead moss.

Leaf litter and dead plant material

Cold, wet conditions do not favour decomposition and, in bogs especially, little takes place. Consequently, partially decomposed materials accumulate as peat. Dry peat even forms out on the open moor because of the lack of earthworms and other major agents of plant decomposition.

Accumulation

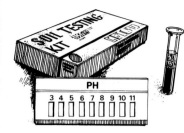

nutrients, especially on sandy soils, which in turn influences the plant community – such deficiencies can also occur because the soil may not have many minerals to start with or it may have them but in forms that are unavailable to plants.

There are many types of soil, often with names indicating the rocks or deposits on which they develop. But the main characteristics that typify soils and the vegetation they support are texture (heavy or light, clayey or sandy, etc.), wetness (dry, wet or waterlogged) and **pH** (acid, neutral or alkaline), as indicated by Figure 3.4.

Climate

Climate is the overriding natural factor in plant and habitat distribution. Rainfall (apart from its effect on soil type) provides the soil moisture that is essential for growth. The level of moisture varies not only from place to place but also throughout the year. Different species of grass can grow in very dry areas, as on southern sandy heaths, and in very wet conditions bordering the blanket bogs of mainly northern, upland areas. Temperature is equally influential as many plants require a particular high summer temperature to flower and fruit while others will succumb to low, prolonged winter temperatures. Temperature is also important in determining both the level of plant production in a year and thus the size of the animal population that can be supported and the activities of decomposers and the release of soil nutrients.

Topography

Topography influences plant distribution through drainage (a major factor in determining soil type), altitude (which influences the climatic conditions) and aspect, which governs the amount of sun received by plants and the degree of exposure to wind. Thus the plant community of a sunny south-facing slope may be quite different to that of a north-facing slope on the same mountain, where the damp, sheltered rocks are never reached by the sun. On high ground, plants have to withstand lower temperatures, higher rainfall, greater water movement in the soil, and increased exposure to wind. Many species grow on the lower mountain grasslands, where soil is plentiful, but few can tolerate the cold winds and stony soils of mountain tops and cliffs.

Ecological processes

Ecology is the study of the relationships of animals and plants to one another and to their surroundings, both living and non-living. That study can encompass the behaviour of individual organisms of a particular species, the population of individuals of a particular species, the community of all living species in an area, and finally the ecosystem comprising the plant and animal communities and their non-living environment.

Competition

Individual organisms are continually competing with other organisms of the same or different species. This competition can be for light, water or nutrients in the case of plants or for food and breeding partners in the case of animals. The need to acquire such resources has led to a wide variety of life strategies and behaviours to ensure the survival of the species. But generally the fate of individual organisms is less important than that of the population as a whole.

Population dynamics

The number of individuals in a population can vary enormously throughout a season and from year to year through the influences of climate, food supply, dispersal and predation. Such short-term fluctuations in numbers can appear alarming but do not indicate in themselves a long-term decline in

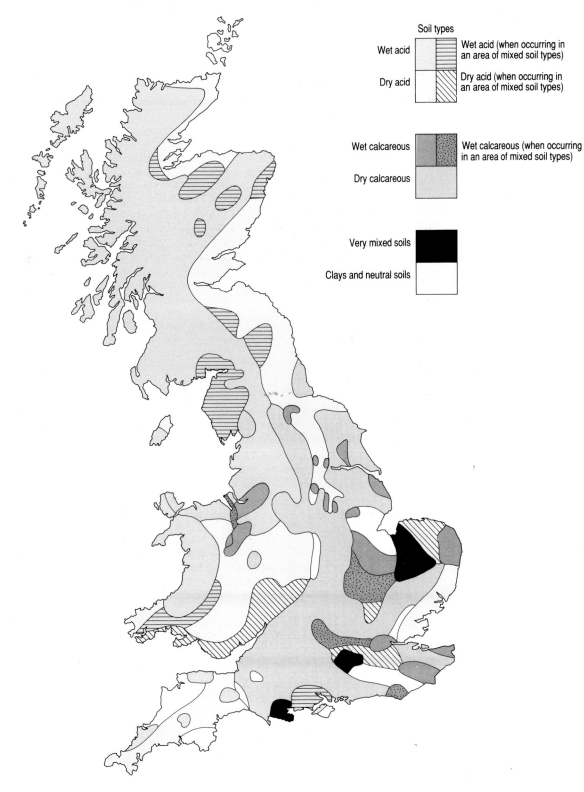

Soil types

Wet acid

Dry acid

Wet acid (when occurring in an area of mixed soil types)

Dry acid (when occurring in an area of mixed soil types)

Wet calcareous

Dry calcareous

Wet calcareous (when occurring in an area of mixed soil types)

Very mixed soils

Clays and neutral soils

Figure 3.4   The major soil types of Great Britian

the 'health' of a habitat, as populations recover when more favourable conditions prevail. Even the total loss of a population is not necessarily a problem because habitats are dynamic and ever-changing, gaining and losing species, and any assessment is a 'snap-shot' of a temporary community. Indeed, no two communities are exactly alike in their species composition although there are recognisable habitats with similar communities and similar environments.

Succession

Communities change over time and, if undisturbed, long-term directional change leads to a **succession** of habitat types. Generally this succession moves from bare ground through a mainly herbaceous plant community, then a mainly shrub plant or scrub community, to a mainly tree community or woodland. The end state of a succession – the **climax community** – is usually relatively stable as a habitat type, even if the community itself changes. Most grasslands, heaths and moors in Great Britain are arrested climaxes in that the grazing, burning or cutting prevents their progression to scrub and then woodland. However, environmental conditions can also prevent the growth of trees and shrubs in coastal or upland areas, where low temperatures and wind restrict tree growth, or on very infertile or toxic soils, or in permanently waterlogged areas.

Age

The longer an ecosystem has existed, the more time it will have had for new plants and animals to immigrate, become established and evolve new interactions, and the greater the chance that rare and specialised plants and animals will have appeared. Indeed, some plant species can be treated as indicators of long-established habitats.

3.2   Wildlife communities of grasslands, heaths and moors

The number and type of plant and animal species that occur on unimproved grasslands, heaths and moors vary with the season, the soil type and the location in Great Britain. While it is the varied plant communities that characterise particular habitats, many of the animal species they contain are also often specific to these habitats, adding yet further to their conservation value.

Calcareous grasslands

Calcareous grasslands are distributed over a variety of geological formations largely composed of calcium carbonate. The majority are found either as downland on chalk or as dry grassland on limestone hills. Indeed, calcareous grasslands usually occur on shallow, well-drained soils with a high organic matter content and a high calcium carbonate content. However, they are also generally poor in other nutrients such as nitrates and phosphates, the lack of which can restrict plant growth. The stresses imposed by a shortage of water and nutrients, coupled with the impact of grazing, leads to a very species-rich community in which no single species becomes dominant. Any change in these factors, especially grazing, leads to a smaller number of species dominating the sward and reducing its richness. Absence of grazing leads to invasion by scrub plants.

Plants

Calcareous grasslands support many plant species, with more than 30 species per square metre in some areas. Although the full list of plant species found on these grasslands is very long and variable from place to place, several plants are found so regularly that they can be used as indicators of these habitats. Many of these indicator species are also **calcicoles**, being more or less restricted to soils rich in calcium, including many rare species, such as most of Great Britain's wild orchids.

The great diversity of grass, sedge and herb plants found in calcareous grasslands supports an equally diverse invertebrate community, many species having specific food plants. A large proportion of British butterflies can be found in these habitats (see Table 3.1 overleaf), as well as moths, grasshoppers and other insects. They are also noted for the wealth of snail species, which require much calcium carbonate to produce their shells.

Neutral grasslands

The communities of neutral habitats have not been studied as much as those of alkaline or acidic soils. They are not as easy to classify by the plant communities that they support and many are described by the agricultural management practices that created them. Thus there are **washlands**, wet alluvial meadows, **flood meadows**, **water meadows**, ridge and furrow old pasture, dales hay meadows and northern grazed meadows, as well as neutral purple moor-grass, tussocky neutral grassland and reverted pasture (or 'tumble down' grassland following arable cultivation).

However, it is still possible to identify many plant species that are typical of these habitats, if not common to most of them. In particular, species that are characteristic of neutral grassland fall into groups which reflect their ability to withstand increasing periods of time under water. There are also marked distinctions between plants such as false oat that are found in tall swards cut for hay and species such as crested dogstail that occur in shorter, grazed swards. Differences in plant species are also caused by latitude. Northern hay meadows have plants which are scarce in the south, such as wood cranesbill which replaces meadow cranesbill. Conversely, many familiar southern woodland species, such as early purple and greater butterfly orchids, are found in northern hay meadows.

Short, grazed swards do not generally support as many invertebrate species, and they certainly support less invertebrate **biomass**, than hay meadows or rough grassland. This is because the greater structural diversity of a tall plant community offers more **niches** for invertebrates to live in, more food to survive on and more time to reproduce, even though there may be fewer plant species present. Early mowing of meadows or rough grassland reduces both the abundance of invertebrates and their ability to reproduce successfully.

Short grassland swards do not provide much cover for nesting birds even though many will feed there; for example, swallows and green woodpeckers (see Table 3.2 overleaf). Longer grass does provide more nesting opportunities for birds such as skylark, lapwing and yellow wagtail, while wet grassland is favoured by snipe and redshank. A much greater variety of feeding and nesting sites occurs as scrub invades grassland to produce a mixed habitat, although they disappear if dense thickets develop.

Lowland heaths

Heaths are not very rich in plant and animal species, but those that do occur there are often most abundant in that habitat.

Table 3.1 A guide to butterflies of grassland, heaths and moors

Species	Larval food plant	Flight time	Distribution
Chalk and limestone grassland slopes			
Adonis blue	Horseshoe vetch	May–Jun, Aug–Sept	S England
Chalkhill blue	Horseshoe vetch	Jul–Sept	S England
Silver-spotted skipper	Sheep's fescue grass	Jul–Aug	S England
Glanville fritillary	Ribwort plantain	May–Jun	IOW only
Chalk and limestone slopes preferred but not exclusively			
Lulworth skipper	Tor grass	Jul–Aug	Dorset, Devon, S England
Small blue	Kidney vetch	May–Jun	S England and Wales (very local)
Brown argus	Common rock-rose	May–Jun, Jun–Sept	S England, N Wales
Northern brown argus	Common rock-rose	Jul–Aug	N England, Scotland
Marbled white	Fescue grasses	Jul–Aug	S England
Dark green fritillary	Common dog violet and other *Viola* spp.	Jul–Aug	Great Britain
Dingy skipper	Birdsfoot trefoil	Apr–Jun	Great Britain
Duke of Burgundy fritillary	*Primula* spp. especially cowslip	May–Jun	S England (very local)
Chalk and limestone slopes and heaths			
Grayling	Fine and medium grasses	Jul–Sept	S and N England, S and W Wales, Scotland (local)
Silver-studded blue	Birdsfoot trefoil Rock-roses Heather Gorses	Jun–Aug	S England, N Wales
Mainly damp meadows			
Marsh fritillary	Devil's-bit scabious	May–Jun	England and Wales (very local)
Damp moors and bogs			
Large heath	White-beaked sedge Purple moor-grass	Jul–Aug	N England, N Wales, Scotland
Scotch argus	Moor grasses	Jun–Jul	NW England, Scotland
Mountain sides			
Mountain ringlet	Mat grass	Jun–Jul	NW England, Scotland
Wide range of grassy and scrub habitats			
Large skipper	Coarse grasses, especially cocksfoot	Jun–Aug	England, Wales
Small skipper	Yorkshire fog and other coarse grasses	Jun–Aug	England, Wales
Essex skipper	Cocksfoot and other coarse grasses	Jul–Aug	SE England
Chequered skipper	Purple moor-grass	May–Jun	Scotland (local)
Wall brown	Coarse grasses	May–Jun, Jul–Aug	England, Wales
Meadow brown	Fescues and meadow grasses	Jun–Jul, Aug–Sept	Great Britain
Small heath	Fine-leaved grasses such as fescues	May–Sept	Great Britain
Common blue	Birdsfoot trefoil Restharrows	May–Jul, Aug–Sept	Great Britain
Small copper	Sorrels	Apr–May, Jul–Aug	Great Britain
Orange-tip	Garlic mustard and *Cardamine* spp.	May–Jun	England, Wales, Scotland (local)
Gatekeeper	Fine- and medium-leaved grasses	Jul–Sept	England, Wales
Green hairstreak	Gorses Rock-roses Birdsfoot trefiol	Apr–Jul	Great Britain
Ringlet	Medium and coarse grasses	Jun–Aug	England, Wales

Table 3.2 A guide to birds of grasslands, heaths and moors

Species	Distribution	Food	Nesting site
Lowland grasslands and heaths			
Kestrel	Resident in Great Britain	Small mammals and birds plus insects and worms	Cliffs, buildings, trees
Hobby	Summer visitor to S England	Small birds plus insects	Trees
Barn owl	Resident in Great Britain	Small mammals and birds plus insects	Cliffs, buildings, trees
Little owl	Resident in England and Wales	Small mammals and birds plus insects and worms	Cliffs, buildings, trees
Stone curlew	Summer visitor to SE England	Invertebrates	Ground
Skylark	Resident in Great Britain	Seeds and other vegetable matter plus invertebrates	Ground
Whitethroat	Summer visitor to Great Britain	Insects	Bushes
Lesser whitethroat	Summer visitor to S England	Insects	Bushes
Red-backed shrike	Rare summer visitor to SE England	Insects, small birds, mammals and reptiles	Bushes
Dartford warbler	Resident mainly Hants. and Dorset	Insects	Bushes
Grasshopper warbler	Summer visitor to Great Britain except N Scotland	Insects	Ground, bushes
Meadow pipit	Resident in Great Britain	Insects	Ground
Tree pipit	Summer visitor to Great Britain	Insects	Ground
Linnet	Resident in Great Britain	Seeds, insects	Bushes
Upland moors			
Hen harrier	Resident in N England, N Wales, Scotland	Small mammals and birds	Ground
Merlin	Resident in SW England, N Britain	Small birds plus insects	Ground, trees, cliffs
Red grouse	Resident in SW England, N Britain	Heather	Ground
Golden plover	Resident in N Britain	Invertebrates plus seeds and berries	Ground
Dunlin	Resident in N Britain	Invertebrates	Ground
Snipe	Resident in Great Britain	Invertebrates plus seeds and grasses	Ground
Curlew	Resident in Great Britain	Invertebrates plus vegetable matter	Ground
Greenshank	Resident in NW Scotland	Invertebrates	Ground
Lapwing	Resident in N and W Britain	Invertebrates plus vegetable matter	Ground
Stonechat	Resident N and W Britain	Insects	Bushes, trees
Ring ouzel	Summer visitor to N and W Britain	Invertebrates, berries	Bushes, buildings
Wheatear	Summer visitor to N and W Britain	Insects	Ground, walls
Twite	Resident in N Britain	Seeds	Ground, bushes

Most of the characteristic plants of heaths are shrubs, and most typical are species of heather. Ling is the most common species but the Cornish heath on heathlands of the Lizard and the Dorset heath on the Isle of Purbeck are very localised. As with many lowland grasslands, reduced grazing leads to bracken and/or scrub invasion as part of a succession.

There are several invertebrates which mainly occur in heaths. These include silver-studded blue and grayling butterflies, common heath, grass emerald and emperor moths, mottled grasshopper, green tiger beetle, heath assassin bug and several solitary wasps and dragonflies.

Most species of reptiles are found on heaths; some also inhabit various types of grassland. Heathland is therefore a very important habitat for reptiles and is the major stronghold of the smooth snake, the slow worm and the sand lizard.

Acidic grasslands and moors

Acidic grasslands are the most widespread type of unsown grassland in Great Britain, but they are nearly all poor in animal and plant species. Nevertheless, they do, along with the heather moors and blanket bog, have several interesting and important species – enough to make many of them of international importance.

Several grass species are found on acid soils but a few species are dominant. In particular, wetter areas usually have mat grass while on drier soils fescue and bent grasses predominate. Where grazing is not too intense the grasses can be dominated by heather. Bilberry, cranberry and cotton grass are often associated with these heather moorlands, and also with blanket bog where various types of bog moss are the most important plant species in the community.

Upland moors are characterised by three butterflies – large heath, small mountain ringlet and Scotch argus – and several moths – northern eggar, netted mountain moth and Rannoch sprawler, for example – which are not found elsewhere in Great Britain. Because of the climate and altitude these and other insect species are often less abundant than at lower altitudes.

Several very different species of bird are particularly characteristic of upland areas; for example, dotterel, golden plover, wheatear, black grouse, merlin, hen harrier and golden eagle. Several species are encouraged by the early stages of upland forestry but are displaced by full afforestation. The most notable bird of heather moorland is the red grouse, the only species that actually feeds on heather.

The wild, open habitats of upland moorland allow several mammals to survive in large numbers, such as red deer, mountain hare, fox and short-tailed vole.

3.3   Habitat assessment criteria

With a basic understanding of grassland, heath and moor ecosystems, as described in Section 3.1, and the species that they support, as outlined in Section 3.2, a detailed assessment of the wildlife value of these habitats can be made. This can never be truly 'objective'. There will always be situations where even experts will disagree, or cases where personal preferences have an important influence. However, a reasonable assessment does provide a picture or profile of the current status of a habitat at a particular point in time and, if repeated, provides a baseline from which to identify natural changes and the effects of management practices. As with other habitats, the following criteria are a useful general guide to the wildlife value of grasslands, heaths and moors:

▷ its naturalness;

▷ its structural and plant species diversity;

▷ the rarity of the species it contains;

▷ its area or size.

As with landscape assessment, assessing the wildlife value of grassland, heath or moor is best done by marking important areas on a map, taking photographs or drawing sketches from recorded positions and making detailed notes describing each area.

If the site has been designated, for example as an SSSI, detailed surveys will already have been made by professional naturalists from the Nature Conservancy Council (NCC) and a copy given to the landowner. Furthermore, most unimproved grasslands of conservation value have been surveyed by local naturalist or wildlife trusts. Even so, it is a good idea to do your own assessment too as you will learn more about the area, and be able to take a more constructive part in its future management.

Naturalness

Few grassland, heath or moor areas can be considered truly natural in the sense of not having been affected significantly by our activities. Indeed, most of them are the result of human interference in the natural succession, leading to arrested climax communities. However, many semi-natural communities are recognised which, whatever their origin (woodland clearance, failed cropping systems), have arisen over considerable periods of time through ecological processes, in particular natural colonisation and grazing pressure. So, although these semi-natural habitats are artificial in one sense, they are natural in another sense through being self-sown and unimproved by artificial means.

Most grassland has become less natural because it has been 'improved' for agriculture by re-seeding with non-native grass species and using fertilisers, herbicides and drainage schemes to increase the productivity of the grass sward and hence the livestock grazing it. At the same time the pressure to increase livestock productivity has led to overgrazing in some areas which in itself has degraded the wildlife value of the habitat, most notably in moorland areas.

The naturalness of grasslands, heaths and moors therefore relates partly to the age and origin of the habitat but also to the degree of disturbance of the normal ecological processes that would shape that habitat, including the process of grazing. Table 3.3 (overleaf) indicates how you could rate grasslands, heaths and moors for naturalness.

Table 3.3   Habitat assessment criteria for grasslands, heaths and moors

Criterion	Rating
1 Naturalness	
Old established (more than 50 years) unimproved grassland, heath or moor	✶✶✶✶
Recently established (less than 50 years) unimproved grassland, heath or moor	✶✶✶
Old established, moderately improved grassland, heath or moor	✶✶
Heavily improved or intensively managed grassland of any age	✶
2 Diversity	
2.1 Structural diversity	
Four-layered grassland, heath or moor with a mosaic of heights	✶✶✶✶
Three-layered grassland, heath or moor with a mosaic of heights	✶✶✶
Two-layered grassland, heath or moor of uniform height	✶✶
Single-layered grassland of uniform height	✶
2.2 Plant species diversity per transect (30 minute walk) in calcareous grasslands	
More than 45 species	✶✶✶✶
Between 31 and 45 species	✶✶✶
Between 16 and 30 species	✶✶
Less than 15 species	✶
2.3 Plant species diversity per transect (30 minute walk) in neutral grasslands	
More than 30 species	✶✶✶✶
Between 21 and 30 species	✶✶✶
Between 11 and 20 species	✶✶
Less than 10 species	✶
2.4 Plant species diversity per transect (30 minute walk) in acidic grasslands, heaths and moors	
More than 15 species	✶✶✶✶
Between 11 and 15 species	✶✶✶
Between 6 and 10 species	✶✶
Less than 5 species	✶
3 Rarity	
3.1 Habitat rarity	
Nationally rare	✶✶✶✶
Regionally rare	✶✶✶
Regionally common but not nationally	✶✶
Nationally and regionally common	✶
3.2 Species rarity	
Containing more than one species of plant and/or animal that is nationally rare	✶✶✶✶
Containing one species of plant and/or animal that is nationally rare	✶✶✶
Containing one or more locally rare plant and/or animal species	✶✶
Containing no species in any of the above categories	✶
4 Area	
Grassland heath or moor that does not score more than ✶ naturalness, or diversity or rarity, regardless of size	O
Grassland, heath or moor more than 10 ha	✶✶✶✶
Grassland, heath or moor between 5 and 10 ha	✶✶✶
Grassland, heath or moor between 2 and 5 ha	✶✶
Grassland, heath or moor less than 2 ha	✶

Diversity

The diversity of a habitat can relate both to the number of plant and/or animal species present and to the structural diversity of the vegetation. This is because animal species diversity depends quite strongly on plant structural diversity.

Grassland is a structurally simple plant community that quite rapidly becomes structurally more complex through succession (see Figure 3.5). Managed heather communities also change over time to produce a structurally diverse habitat (see Box 3.1 overleaf). In general, the greater structural diversity of lowland heath, heather moorland and scrub habitats provides more potential niches for the animal community than grassland. Conversely, the first effects of removing grazing animals is a drop in plant species diversity as the most vigorous grasses are no longer held in check by grazing and tend to out-compete the other plant species.

Structural diversity

Tree layer, canopy or overstorey

Shrub layer or understorey

Herb or field layer

Ground layer

Figure 3.5   The structure of grasslands, heaths and moors

Plant species diversity or density (see 'Area' below) is influenced by many factors. It generally increases with time, along with the probability that any given species will invade a site that is suitable for establishment. Older grasslands are therefore richer in species than younger ones (see 'Naturalness' above). The composition of temporary leys, sown as part of an arable rotation with a grass–clover seed mixture, and ploughed every three to five years, allows little opportunity for invasion and diversification by other species. Their wildlife value is consequently low.

Plant species diversity

The physical and chemical status of the soil, as noted earlier, is a very important factor. High levels of nutrients, particularly nitrogen, promote the dominance of a few grasses, so that many of the smaller herbs tend to be excluded and a species-poor community results. So, provided that minimum levels of nutrients are available, poorer soils support a higher species diversity, since limited nutrients prevent the vigorous growth of potential dominants. The availability of nutrients is also influenced by pH, soil depth and soil moisture. Most soils contain enough calcium for plant growth but calcareous soils are constantly saturated with an alkaline solution of lime that can immobilise nutrients. Thus alkaline soils often have a higher plant diversity than acid soils. Similarly, a shallow soil limits the vigour and competitiveness of those species which would become dominant on deeper soil to the exclusion of many others. Lastly, high rainfall can leach and so reduce soil nutrient availability, but very dry and very wet situations in themselves also impose stresses on plant growth and can lead to a higher plant diversity.

Box 3.1   The structural dynamics of heather: phases of the life cycle

During their life span, heather plants change gradually in size, morphology and growth habit as they undergo physiological ageing and become less vigorous. Four distinct phases are usually recognised (see Figure 3.6).

1   The earliest phase is the 'pioneer' phase, when young plants are established from seeds or new shoots sprout from buds at the base of the charred stems remaining after a fire. During this period, plants are discrete, less than 15 centimetres tall, cover the ground incompletely, and have a higher concentration of nutrients (especially nitrogen and phosphorus) in their shoots than they do in subsequent phases.

2   Heather plants pass next into a 'building' phase, when they grow vigorously, become finely branched, develop a dense canopy of bright green shoots, and may eventually cover the ground so completely that almost all other plants species disappear. At this stage, plants are up to about 30 centimetres tall and there is a very high density of stems rooting at ground level – sometimes 2000 or more per square metre.

3   Vigour is much reduced in the 'mature' phase. Plants become 'leggy' with long thick stems and in the canopy there is much more inedible woody material than green shoots. The plants tend to be top heavy and the branches begin to fall outwards so that height does not usually exceed 40–50 centimetres. As some stems die and others thicken, density declines to less than 1000 stems per square metre.

4   Finally, plants become 'degenerate'. By this stage, the central branches are often prostrate and dying. There may now be less than 250 stems per square metre, and plant height is usually less than 40 centimetres. Sometimes the outer branches may 'layer' (i.e. root where they touch the ground), in which case they continue growing with renewed vigour.

There are no set ages at which heather passes from one phase to the next. Where annual production is slow, because of a cold climate, poor soil or heavy grazing, ageing is retarded and plants may take 40 years or more to reach the degenerate phase. Conversely, rapid production entails rapid ageing and degeneracy may be reached in less than 20 years.

Figure 3.6   The growth phases of heather

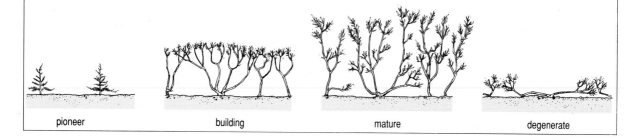

| pioneer | building | mature | degenerate |

A high plant diversity is often accompanied by a high invertebrate species diversity but not so much by a high vertebrate density. This is because birds, reptiles and mammals prefer a greater structural diversity to a greater species diversity. Detailed ratings for plant species diversity, which is usually easier to assess than more mobile animals, are given in Table 3.3.

Rarity

The term rarity can refer both to species and to habitats. Lowland heath and semi-natural chalk downland are now rare habitats in Great Britain and are therefore very highly valued. Because of the rarity of these habitats, many of the species that depend on them have also become rare. For instance, despite occupying a small proportion of lowland Great Britain, semi-natural grasslands support about 550 species of flowering plants (about one-quarter of the total British flora). Of these species 81 can be considered rare because they occur in less than 15 of the 2900 10-km^2 squares that comprise the National Grid (see Table 3.4). Similarly, the insects and other animals that live off these plants have also become rare. Silver-spotted skipper, small blue and Adonis blue butterflies, for instance, have all contracted in their distribution in the past few decades to the stage where they are rare and possibly endangered.

Table 3.3 shows how you can assess a grazed habitat on the basis of the number of rare animals and/or plant species that it contains. This does require proper identification of species and if you are at all uncertain of doing this, contact a professional biologist or a competent amateur naturalist. Members of local Wildlife Trusts are usually willing to help (see the *Helpful Organisations* booklet in the foundation module). As plants flower and animals appear at different times of the year, you may need to survey a site at several different times to get a more complete picture. The use of a standard assessment procedure, such as doing a count of plants or animals over a 30 minute period, will allow you to compare one site with another and to monitor changes at the same site over time.

Area

Larger habitats tend to support a greater number of species than smaller ones. Every species requires a certain area which must be exceeded if it is to maintain a viable population. Clearly, a larger habitat will satisfy the minimum area requirements of a greater number of species. Larger areas are also likely to be more diverse in topography, soil depth, moisture and nutrient status, which will tend to enhance plant species diversity.

Table 3.4 Some rare and endangered plants of lowland calcareous grasslands, neutral grasslands and acidic heaths and grasslands

Calcareous grassland		Neutral grassland	Acidic heath and grassland
Man orchid	Wild candytuft	Downy-fruited sedge	Yellow centaury
Musk orchid	Small restharrow	Whorled caraway	Mossy stonecrop
Lizard orchid	Chalk milkwort	Fritillary	Cornish heath
Fen orchid	Dwarf milkwort	Yellow star-of-Bethlehem	Dorset heath
Late spider orchid	Spiny cinquefoil	Summer snowflake	Marsh gentian
Early spider orchid	Pasque flower	Corky-fruited water dropwort	Heath lobelia
Military orchid	Meadow clary	Narrow-leaved water dropwort	Bog hair-grass
Monkey orchid	Field fleawort	Lesser butterfly orchid	Brown beaksedge
Burnt orchid	Moon carrot	Adder's tongue spearwort	Marsh clubmoss
Round-headed leek	Nottingham catchfly	Viper's grass	Pillwort
Ground pine	Cut-leaved germander	Cambridge milk parsley	
Mountain everlasting	Lesser meadow rue	Sulphur clover	
Bristol rock-cress	Bastard toadflax	Upright vetch	
Goldilocks	Perfoliate penny-cress		
Great pignut	Honewort		
Tuberous thistle	Spiked speedwell		
Maiden pink	Spiked rampion		
Cheddar pink	Perennial flax		
Dark-red helleborine	Somerset grass		
Slender bedstraw	Heath sedge		
Chiltern gentian	Dwarf sedge		
Early gentian	Birds-foot sedge		
White rock-rose	Hutchinsia		
Hoary rock-rose	Spotted catsear		

(Source: Wells and Sheail, 1988)

Species–area effects can be diminished by isolation of the habitat. Even a large habitat will suffer if it is remote from similar habitats because there are always populations that will become extinct in a particular area for one reason or another, and isolation by too big a distance prevents the recolonisation by that species or colonisation by a different species to maintain species numbers. Therefore, isolated habitats have fewer species than habitats of the same size that are in close proximity to similar habitats. Ratings for area as an assessment criterion are given in Table 3.3.

3.4   Making your own habitat assessment

A general habitat assessment form is described in Chapter 3 of the foundation book, and it is used in the case studies in Section 3.5. The form provides a broad overview of the habitat's wildlife value. A more detailed checklist using the four criteria described in Section 3.3 is also shown in Section 3.5. These criteria overlap to some extent because of their interrelationships (see Box 3.2). Remember that these ratings are subjective in that a habitat scoring four stars on size is not necessarily twice as good as one that rates two stars. What they do is provide a profile of features which can be used both to assess the current status of a habitat and to monitor its development under a particular management regime. For example, species diversity might be increased by selective mowing, so that in unmown or infrequently mown areas longer grass and possibly some scrub invasion will be encouraged; or by spreading herb-rich hay bales over poor quality grassland; or by reducing stocking density and hence overgrazing. In each case, comparison of the existing rating for diversity with the original one will allow you to judge whether changed management has achieved its aim.

Fill in a general habitat assessment profile for your site, concentrating on the areas of grassland, heath and moor (or fill in one for each distinct area if there are more than one) as shown in Table 3.6. Supplement this with more detail on the different criteria as suggested in Table 3.3, using a checklist like the one shown in Tables 3.5 and 3.7.

3.5   Habitat assessment of case study areas

Borders hill farm

The case study farm exhibits a range of habitats from the upland vegetation that is typical of hill farms in the area to more local and regionally rare communities of plants meriting SSSI status (see Figure 3.8).

The typical habitats of the area are as follows.

Approximately 60% of the farm area is heather moorland – dominated by heath species: ling, bell heather and bilberry with occasional patches of crowberry. In certain areas bracken forms dense stands and has expanded its range over the last 20 years. In the adjacent hollows and openings in older heather are associated grasses such as wavy hair-grass, tussocks of mat grass, bent and fescue species, with tormentil, lady's bedstraw, heath bedstraw, and occasional harebell, wood rush, and rowan regeneration; and mosses carpeting the ground under the heaths. There are occasional ferns, such as *Dryopteris* species and hard fern.

Box 3.2 Habitat area, species diversity and rarity

Within broad limits, the larger an area sampled, the more species are found in it. It is, however, of interest to know how rapidly new species are encountered as a sampling area is increased.

If you examine Figure 3.7 you will see that there is a decelerating rate of increase in species numbers as area increases. Small increments in sampling area add many more species to the sample when the area sampled is small than when it is large.

The relationship shown in Figure 3.7 is a common one for samples taken within a relatively homogeneous habitat such as a meadow. The slope of the curve declines as area is increased because the number of possible species in the habitat is limited. Note, however, that a few new species were still being found, even when the sampling area had reached 1 hectare (10000 square metres).

The 1 hectare sample of Purwell Meadow for which data are given in Figure 3.7 contained 153 species. When a second hectare was added (not plotted on Figure 3.7), the 2 hectare sample contained 176 species. Assuming that species in the meadow are not clumped in their distribution, these data indicate that there are at least 23 species whose abundance could well be less than one individual per hectare. Or, in other words, there are many rare species in the meadow.

However, we must assume (or better still confirm) that species are not clumped before drawing conclusions about the abundance of rare species in Purwell Meadow! This is because the 23 'rare' species may actually be abundant, but clumped somewhere in the second half of the 2 hectare sample and absent from the first hectare. If so, the true abundance of the species would be much more than an average of one individual per hectare.

This is why it is suggested that species numbers are counted over a 30 minute transect or walk rather than by marked-out metre-square plots.

(Source: Open University, S326 *Ecology*, Unit 14, p. 7)

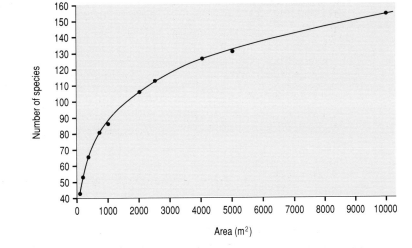

Figure 3.7 Species–area curve for numbers of species in Purwell Meadow, Hertfordshire

In the steep cleuchs (gullies) there are scattered remnants of broad-leaved woodland with birch, alder, rowan, willow species, dog rose and hawthorn. In the long heather rowan, willow and birch regeneration is common, as are mountain fern and the herbs wood sage and devil's-bit scabious.

Scattered throughout the heather mosaic are wetter areas or 'flushes' that are dominated by sharp-flowered rush or, less commonly, soft rush and eared willow. Associated grasses include tufted hair-grass, Yorkshire fog, sweet vernal-grass and purple moor-grass with marsh thistle, lesser stitchwort and germander speedwell.

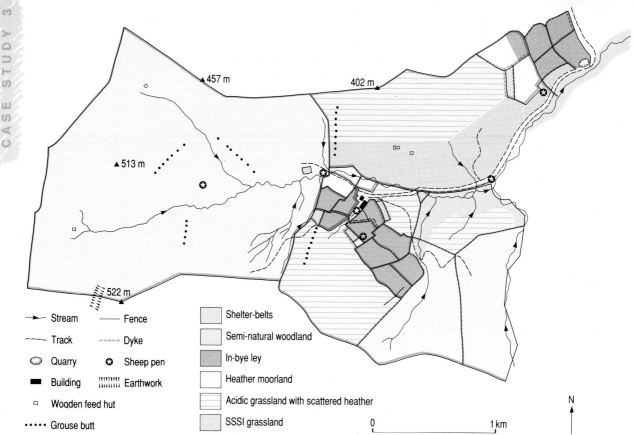

Figure 3.8   Habitats on the Borders hill farm

On the higher and poorly drained podsol soils, species that are characteristic of a blanket bog community appear; for example, cotton grass, sedge, mosses and heath rush.

Apart from the soil and climatic conditions, the presence or absence of the above species and their frequency within a plant community are further complicated by the burning and grazing pressures on the area.

Habitat assessment profiles for two selected sites (not included here) demonstrate a marked difference in vegetation composition and structure caused by burning. Only those few species which respond to burning appear initially. As the vegetation structure builds up so a variety of micro-climates are created which in turn become colonised by a wider variety of grasses, herbs, etc. This difference is also very apparent in the checklist of habitat assessment criteria (see Table 3.5).

Stelling Minnis Common

Kent Trust for Nature Conservation Site of Nature Conservation Interest (SNCI), grade 1 on 27 hectares.

Notable species: Western gorse at its most easterly site in south England and one of the three only recorded sites in Kent.

Plant list: more than 200 species in 1990 (ongoing survey).

Also mammals (e.g. badger, fallow deer, field and short-tailed voles, pygmy and common shrews, wood and yellow-necked mice), reptiles (adder is common), butterflies (meadow brown, small heath, small copper, small skipper, red admiral) (NB: not comprehensive survey information).

Table 3.5 Habitat assessment checklist for (a) an unburned and (b) a recently burned area of heather moorland on the Borders hill farm

Date

Criterion	Rating*	
	(a)	(b)
1 Naturalness	***	**
2 Diversity		
2.1 Species	****	*
2.2 Structural	****	**
3 Rarity		
3.1 Habitat	**	**
3.2 Species	*	*
4 Area	****	****

* See Table 3.3.

Stelling Minnis Common supports an interesting mosaic of habitats: small areas of developing woodland interspersed with more open areas of grassland (the traditional appearance of the Common); and areas of bracken and scrub which have encroached since grazing ceased.

Grassland – the slightly acidic soils support a range of heathland plants, e.g. ling, heath bedstraw, harebell, tormentil, and grasses such as fine bent and red fescue.

Woodland – secondary and mainly oak with ash, field maple and hornbeam, and birch throughout.

Scrub – mainly gorse, hawthorn and dogwood.

Bracken – dense in areas and apparently increasing; the decline in heather is probably due to this.

Management

The main problem in managing the Common is to achieve a balance between the value of the open grass (heath) areas and the developing wood and scrub habitats. Control of grass and bracken is needed; mowing is not ideal, and will not discourage bracken. A small area is cut as a hay meadow. Clearance of scrub is thought to be vital by some interests, e.g. graziers; to other interests any intervention is vandalism.

Kent Trust for Nature Conservation (KTNC) has drawn up a conservation management plan for the Common which divides it into 15 areas.

The (simplified) case study map divides Stelling Minnis Common into seven areas (Figure 3.9). (Again, this is somewhat arbitrary, as scrub, trees and pockets of woodland are scattered throughout.) The habitat assessment profile (see Table 3.6) was done in part of the open grass and scrub area. It is fairly typical of the open grass areas, with their margins of woodland and scrub and scattered individual trees. Table 3.7 is a more detailed habitat assessment checklist.

Table 3.6 Habitat assessment profile for Stelling Minnis Common

Land holding _Stelling_   Habitat type _Lowland_   Habitat number   Date _15·8·91_

A _Physical features_ _Minnis Common_   _Heath_   _Part of AREA (9) (KTNC Survey)_

1 Land use   Past uses _GRAZING_   Present uses _AMENITY_

2 Physical conditions

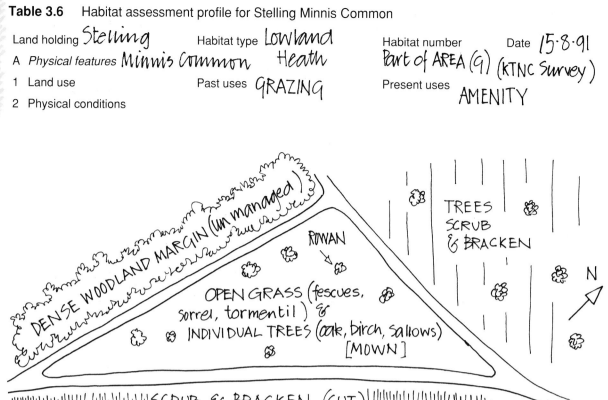

Terrain   (Flat) sloping, undulating

Age   < 5 years, 5–10 years, 10–50 years, (> 50 years)

Area   < 0.5 ha, 0.5–1 ha, (1–5 ha,) > 5 ha

Soil wetness   (Well drained) occasionally water-logged, always water-logged

Soil texture   Silty, sandy, (clayey)

Soil chemistry   (Acidic) neutral, alkaline

B _Wildlife features_

1 Vegetation cover   (* = present; ** = moderately common; *** = frequent)

   Mosses *   Grasses * * *   Shrubs * * *

   Ferns * * *   Herbs * *   Trees * *

2 Animals   (* = present; ** = moderately common; *** = frequent)

   Insects * *   Amphibians   Birds * * *

   Molluscs   Reptiles * *   Mammals * *

3 Habitat assessment criteria (* = low value; ** = moderate value; *** = high value)

   Diversity   Naturalness   Rarity   Area   } _see Table 3·7_

C _Land use features_ (* = low value; ** = moderate value; *** = high value)

   Wildlife * * *   Education * *   Forestry

   Recreation * * *   Agriculture   Industry

D _Summary assesssment_ _See notes (section 3.5)_

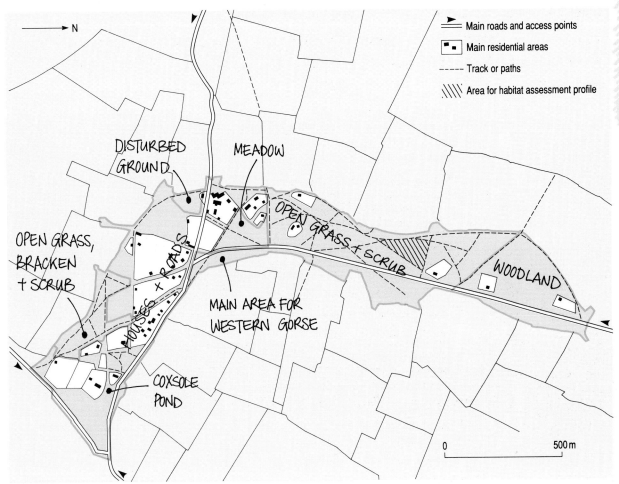

Legend:
- Main roads and access points
- Main residential areas
- ----- Track or paths
- \\\\\ Area for habitat assessment profile

Figure 3.9 Habitat assessment for Stelling Minnis Common

Table 3.7 Habitat assessment checklist for Stelling Minnis Common

Date

Criterion	Rating*
1 Naturalness	✱✱✱✱
2 Diversity	
2.1 Species	✱✱✱✱
2.2 Structural	✱✱✱✱
3 Rarity	
3.1 Habitat	✱✱✱
3.2 Species	✱
4 Area	✱✱✱✱

* See Table 3.3.

Chapter 4

BUSINESS AND INTEGRATED ASSESSMENT

In this chapter you will be shown how to assess the current commercial or business values of grasslands, heaths and moors on a holding, how these interact with the landscape and conservation interests, and how the various assessments may be integrated.

The commercial uses of grasslands, heaths and moors fall into three broad categories. The greatest use is as a source of food for grazing animals either feeding directly on the growing crop or feeding on a harvested product such as **hay** or **silage**.

In some areas grazing extends to the shrub-dominated heathland, particularly upland moorland, and to different animals, notably red deer and red grouse. Both of these wild species are actively managed, mainly for sport as game animals.

Many grazed areas, particularly unenclosed commons and uplands, are also a source of recreation and other enjoyment, sometimes in conflict with the primary use. However, a growing proportion of grassland is specifically devoted to amenity use as urban parks, domestic gardens, sports grounds, golf courses, country parks and nature reserves, although some of these uses are not always compatible with landscape or wildlife conservation.

A business assessment of a site allows potential conflicts to be identified and taken into account in the preparation of an integrated conservation management plan.

4.1   Business assessment

In assessing the uses of grassland it is worth reflecting on the value of grass to people, to suit their different needs. Grass is important, first, because there are species that are suitable for every climatic zone in Great Britain and, secondly, because grasses can withstand regular removal of leaves by animals or by machines. Thirdly, many grasses can also withstand trampling by animals or people, and can recolonise gaps in the vegetation cover by **vegetative reproduction**.

Lastly, an important aspect of grass is its effect on soil structure. Grass forms a dense cover of vegetation above the soil (the sward), which prevents erosion by run-off water. Below ground it forms a dense mass of roots which, when they die and decay, increase the organic matter content of the soil and also help to produce a favourable crumb structure in the soil (the vegetation and the soil mass attached to the roots comprise the turf). Crumb structure affects the water-holding properties of the soil, so that a soil with a good structure has a high available water content. The increased organic matter content of the soil also provides a readily available reserve of mineral nutrients for any crop grown on that land, as discussed below.

Grass as a crop

Unlike other crops, a crop of grass only rarely consists of a single grass species and usually includes species other than grasses. There are two categories of grass crop, temporary (or ley) grassland and permanent grassland, the distinction depending on the length of time for which the crop remains on the same area of land. If the grassland is ploughed up and replaced or resown at intervals of less than five years, it is termed temporary. Permanent grassland is that which has not been disturbed by ploughing for at least five years, and may have lain undisturbed for several hundred years. Many of the older grasslands will not have been sown but have developed from existing self-sown vegetation.

Victorian farmers believed in safety in numbers, not only in the size of their families but also in the composition of their grass-seed mixtures, which usually included a little of everything in the seeds catalogue. Since that time there has been a marked swing towards the simplification of seed mixtures and it is now unusual for more than four or five different species and varieties to be included in even the most complex of mixtures. A mixture of species is often used in preference to a single species in order to even out the annual pattern of production within a given grass crop which arises from differences in the growth pattern of the different species, and from differing responses to adverse weather conditions. However, research has largely determined which species or set of species are most valuable agriculturally, and it has also shown that permanent grassland, which usually has a wide range of species, can be as productive as temporary grassland, which has a known, sown, species composition.

The important characteristics of a grass crop are:

1   the amount of dry matter which can be harvested from it;

2   the quality of that dry matter as feed for animals;

3   the seasonal pattern of production of the dry matter.

Additionally, since most grasses are grown in mixtures of species, it is useful to know how different species, or **cultivars** of species, will interact. The competitive ability of a grass cultivar involves its growth rate relative to other species, its tolerance of grazing and trampling by animals, and its tolerance of frost. A species or cultivar which has a high competitive ability, for whatever reason, may tend to suppress other, less aggressive species or cultivars in a mixed grass sward and so become dominant.

The grass crop does not directly supply any food for humans, since its major constituent, cellulose, is not utilisable by the human digestive system. Grass only enters the food supply via animals which can graze and digest grass readily, such as sheep and cattle. Horses, goats, deer and rabbits can also all digest the cellulose of grasses. This digestion is achieved by bacteria in specialised parts of the digestive tract. Sheep and cattle in Great Britain obtain about two-thirds of their total energy requirement and most of their protein requirement from grass. The use of grass as a crop, therefore, depends on the characteristics of both the crop and the grazing animals.

Grazing animals select their food using the senses of touch, taste, sight and smell. They tend to select the more leafy portion of a sward but they may also choose immature seed heads partly because these are more accessible.

49

The 'palatability' of pasture is difficult to assess. However, green succulent material and material with a high sugar content is usually preferred, while dead, mature or mouldy material is usually rejected. Sheep and calves with smaller mouthparts are more selective than larger **ruminants**. Grazing animals tend to avoid pasture that is fouled by, or near to, faeces of their own species. Whether they can do so depends on the abundance of pasture, and competition for feed. More details on grazing behaviour are covered in Section 5.1.

Grass growth

The pattern of growth of most grasses in Great Britain is similar: growth starts early in the spring. During the early period of growth each plant produces **tillers** profusely, many of which then stop producing leaves and develop a flower head (see Figure 4.1). Once this head has matured growth falls markedly as the production of non-flowering, daughter tillers is suppressed by those which flower, causing a reduction in new leaf production during the summer. In the autumn growth recovers slightly, but does not reach as high a level as in the spring.

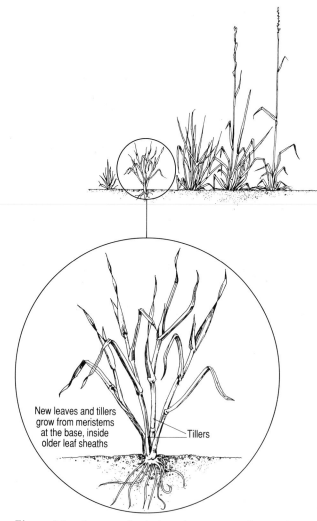

New leaves and tillers grow from meristems at the base, inside older leaf sheaths

Tillers

Figure 4.1   A grass plant at various stages of growth

In the spring most of the increase in dry weight is in the form of leaf, but when flower heads are formed the grass stem becomes thickened with lignin, which cannot be digested by animals. Thus, although the weight of grass increases, its nutritive value (expressed as its digestibility or **D-value**) decreases.

An obvious problem for grazing management is the provision of feed during the winter, when grass is not growing (see Figure 4.2).

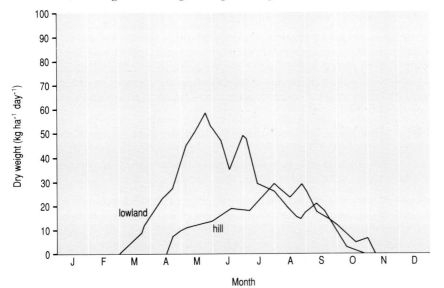

Figure 4.2   The patterns of growth of a grass species at sea level and at 300 metres above sea level in Great Britain

Animals have to eat throughout the year; their daily need for feed per hectare will depend on the number of animals grazing that hectare, and their individual sizes and physiological status. The common ruminants (cows and sheep) tend to reproduce about once a year. For sheep this usually occurs in the spring; cattle often calve throughout the year, but mainly in the spring and autumn. Thus, for a flock of sheep, the total demand for feed per hectare has the general shape shown in Figure 4.3. The decline in demand in the autumn occurs when the majority of lambs are slaughtered, leaving a parent population. For cattle the cycle of demand is more complex, but overall the pattern is as shown in Figure 4.3.

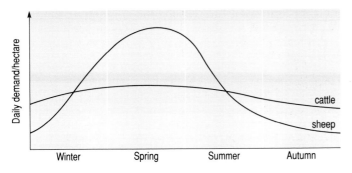

Figure 4.3   Daily demand for feed of typical sheep and cattle populations

In the absence of human interference, ruminants survive over the winter by eating material which has accumulated during the preceding months – although there is no net growth during the winter, grass which grew in the autumn does not immediately disappear, and can be grazed later in the year. Although Figure 4.2 indicates that grasses produce no net growth during the winter, they do still go on producing leaves, but as each new leaf is produced, so the oldest leaf dies off. Although this replacement results in no net change in the amount of grass present, grazing animals can harvest some of this material before it dies, even at this time.

The human manager of ruminants on grassland is faced with a choice: either keep only as many animals per hectare as can survive in the winter on current growth plus any carry-over of surplus leaf from the summer; or find some way of supplementing the available supply in winter, in order to carry enough livestock to use a large proportion of the summer growth.

Very broadly, the choice made depends on the locality and type of grassland involved. If the grassland is relatively flat and accessible, some of the summer surplus can be cut and stored for use in the winter. If this is difficult, only as many animals as can be overwintered successfully are carried, so that some of the summer production is wasted.

Grass conservation

Grass can be stored or **conserved** as hay or silage. Hay or dried grass involves drying the fresh material to a moisture content of less than 15%, which limits further deterioration. Silage is formed by fermentation of the soluble sugars that are present in grass by bacteria, under *anaerobic* conditions, i.e. where oxygen is excluded. This is achieved most effectively by storing the freshly cut, or slightly wilted, material in a sealed tower or *silo*. More often, a horizontal heap or *clamp* of material is constructed, the heap is rolled to expel as much air as possible, and then the surface is covered with a rubber or plastic sheet to exclude the air. Recently the use of large plastic bags to contain the silage has increased.

Conserving grass as silage is slightly less efficient than hay-making, but because the grass can be stored immediately after cutting, it is more reliable than the weather-dependent process of field drying. Well over 50% of all grass conserved in Great Britain is now in the form of silage.

Feeding calculations using stored materials such as hay or silage for the winter feeding of livestock are relatively simple. In the summer, when the animals are grazing, such calculations are more complex, since the method of grazing also has to be considered.

Grazing management

There is an interaction between grazing and the feeding of an animal during the non-grazing period, since, at some time during the growing season, forage has to be cut and conserved for use at other times of the year. In addition, the quantity of hay or silage made is likely to affect the quantity of forage available for grazing.

In theory, it should be possible to estimate exactly how much of the year's forage production needs to be conserved by combining Figures 4.2 and 4.3. The *area* under the growth curve represents the annual total growth; similarly, the area under the curve of animal requirement represents the total amount required per annum. By raising or lowering the requirement curve (i.e. by changing stock numbers), it should be possible to make the two areas equal as in Figure 4.4. The curve also represents daily requirement per hectare. By adjusting the numbers of animals kept per hectare the curve can

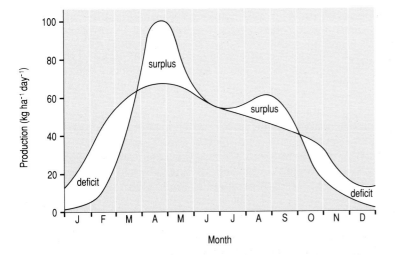

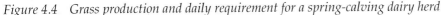

Figure 4.4   Grass production and daily requirement for a spring-calving dairy herd

be moved up or down. Silage or hay can be made during the periods when daily grass growth exceeds daily requirement, i.e. in May–June and possibly in September.

In this all-forage system, the quantity of hay or silage made has to equal the shaded area in Figure 4.4. For the rest of the year, the daily growth increment is assumed to be removed daily. In practice, there are many more decisions to be made, about the exact time of cutting grass for conservation as hay or silage, and the method of grazing. First, while it is possible, in theory, that each day the animals graze exactly that day's grass growth increment, it is clearly impracticable to cut grass every day for hay or silage. Generally, only two or three cuts per year are taken. This means that grass accumulates in the field before cutting and, as it accumulates, it changes in character, becoming less digestible over the early period when the grasses produce flower stems, which contain more lignin than the leaves.

Secondly, although the greatest total yield of nutrients from the herbage can be obtained by a single late cut, this comprises conserved material of relatively low digestibility, which may not be sufficient to provide feed of high enough quality throughout the winter for the animals. Indeed, the overall conversion efficiency of the system may be higher when producing less forage through several cuts, but in a more digestible form. The exact optimum for a given farm depends on circumstances.

Grazing management offers a further series of choices. In theory, the ideal grazing system would exactly balance daily forage growth and removal rate. This situation could be achieved, again in theory, with a range of different *amounts* of grass on offer to the animals. However, the amount of herbage offered affects the rate of removal. It also, incidentally, may affect the rate of herbage growth.

So, in practice, grazing management is not simple. The relationship between amount of herbage present, removal rate, growth rate and loss through senescence and decay of ungrazed leaves is still a topic of research. In addition, the method of grazing can be varied – the animals can be allowed to range freely over the area (set stocking or continuous grazing) or they can be confined to limited areas and made to graze different areas in rotation (see Section 5.1).

In ruminant management, a large degree of control of animals and their feed supply is possible. However, on uncultivatable and sometimes inaccessible land such as the uplands the fundamental problem of matching animal need and supply is still present, but less can be done about it. Conservation of hay or silage may be impossible. Figure 4.2 showed that the growing season in upland areas is more restricted, and the seasonal peak growth rate is lower than on lowlands. This effect is accentuated by shortages of plant nutrients. The most that can be done is to try to increase the total production of herbage by applying some fertiliser, or possibly by limited sowing of **legumes**, such as clover, and to restrict the movement of grazing animals.

Thus, on the lowlands, conservation of surplus summer grass, obtained by using high levels of fertiliser, is used to maintain many animals per unit area of land. By paying attention to cutting and grazing management the aim is to maintain a high level of animal production per unit area, by maintaining high intakes of feed, supplemented in the winter with cereals. In the extensive grazing areas animal numbers per unit area are smaller and limited by the available herbage during winter. Conversion efficiency is increased as far as possible by ensuring adequate supplies of feed from the available herbage or by supplementation at critical periods in the livestock population's life cycle, with the limited supplementation ensuring that reasonable use is made of forage growth in times of surplus, by allowing greater stock numbers per hectare to be kept.

Fertiliser use

In common with other crops, the important nutrients for grass are nitrogen, phosphorus and potassium, but the needs of the crop are rather more complex to determine. If the crop is grazed, most of the potassium removed by the animals is returned in their dung and urine, but most of the phosphorus is retained by them. When cut for hay or silage both nutrients are removed with the crop. Yield and its distribution during the year are mainly determined by the availability of nitrogen and the level of regeneration. In addition to the effect on total yield, the timing of application of nitrogen fertiliser also affects the patterns of grass growth. In general, where a field is to be grazed throughout the year, small regular applications of nitrogen fertiliser are best. Where a field is to be cut in early summer for hay, a single application in the spring is preferable.

In practice, spreading fertiliser costs money so it has to be done as few times a year as possible. Furthermore, the economic return only comes much later, after the grass has been eaten and the animals sold, while there is also unpredictability in the response of grassland to nitrogen fertiliser (although not as unpredictable as production from grass–clover swards). Nitrogen can, in addition, be supplied by leguminous forage crops, such as clover or lucerne. Clover can fix up to 150 kilograms of nitrogen per hectare per annum in Great Britain, which is about equal to the average rate of application of nitrogen fertiliser. Unfortunately, the introduction of clover causes several problems; it is difficult to manage a sward containing both grass and clover so that neither becomes dominant. The maximum yield of an unfertilized, grass–clover mixed sward is less than a heavily fertilised, pure grass sward, while applications of fertiliser tend to suppress the clover, so that its benefit is lost. Nitrogen fertiliser is more effective because its use can be more readily controlled compared to managing grass–clover swards.

The use of pesticides for insect and disease control is limited in grasslands.
There are two reasons for this. First, grass is one of the few plants that can
survive regular grazing, from a height of 20–30 centimetres almost to ground
level. Very few weeds apart from other grasses can survive this treatment.
Relatively little is known about the productivity of weed grasses under
grazing, but it is probably not far short of that of the sown species. Secondly,
because the financial output from grass is unpredictable, except in the dairy
sector, there is little incentive to apply expensive agrochemicals to control
pests or diseases, although there is some evidence that yield increases of up
to 20% could sometimes be achieved by these means.

Game management

Grasslands, heaths and moors all provide areas in which game animals can
flourish. However, the majority (pheasants, partridges, and hares), although
found in such areas, also need hedgerows or woodland edge habitats in
which to feed or breed. The only game species confined to one habitat is the
red grouse on heather moors. Red deer can breed in open moorland, forests
or both.

The red grouse is a sub-species of the widely distributed willow grouse,
which occurs throughout much of Europe and even Asia. It differs from the
other sub-species in not moulting to a white plumage for the winter months
and in feeding mainly on heather. Under very favourable conditions red
grouse can reach extremely high densities of up to 750 birds per square
kilometre. These characteristics have encouraged upland landowners to
manage red grouse populations and produce a surplus of birds which can be
harvested each autumn. Previously, grouse shooting was mainly a sport of
large landowners but with increased economic pressures and a high level of
demand many estate owners now let their grouse shooting for commercial
gain. Grouse moors cover 1.5 million hectares of Great Britain and commercial grouse shooting is an important land use in many upland areas.

Red grouse feed predominantly on heather so their distribution is restricted
to heather moorlands. The productivity of heather moors for red grouse
varies from the drier moors on the east side of Great Britain with higher
densities of red grouse (an average of 50 pairs per square kilometre) to the
wet and less productive moors in the west where grouse densities can be as
low as 2.5 pairs per square kilometre. Variations in red grouse populations
from moor to moor depend on several factors: burning management, grazing intensity by sheep and red deer, predator and parasite control and the
underlying rocks. (Moors on lime-rich rocks are more productive than those
on lime-poor rocks such as granite.)

Productive heather is maintained by controlled burning and careful grazing.
If these practices are neglected or badly managed then the heather moorland
can be replaced by vegetation which is not exploited by grouse and is often
of little value to sheep farming. Nearly all grouse moors are used as rough
grazing for hill farming as well as for grouse shooting.

Heather is a fairly indigestible plant with a high fibre content and low
protein level. To survive and breed successfully grouse must extract the
limited nutrients efficiently, particularly before and during egg laying when
the birds' requirements are greatest. The burning of heather generally results
in a twofold increase in protein content, which steadily decreases to the pre-
burning level within about eight years.

In contrast, heather is not a preferred food of sheep but its value lies in its availability as a green food during the winter months, when the preferred grasses are exhausted and/or covered during snowy weather. Under optimal conditions heather thrives with moderate grazing; it encourages shoot production, and sheep droppings help to fertilise and improve the nutritive quality of the plant. On the other hand, heavy grazing, where 80% of the current season's growth is removed, suppresses shoot production, reduces the plant's reserves and gives it a characteristic gnarled appearance (see Box 4.1). The effects of overgrazing in combination with the uprooting of young shoots and bruising of the plant through trampling can lead rapidly to the loss of heather.

Box 4.1   The effects of heavy grazing on heather growth

It is not unusual for the tips of heather shoots to die over winter because of the severity of the weather. Indeed, this produces the characteristic branching pattern of heather which maintains the density of shoots in the canopy as the bush grows larger. However, extensive or early death of plant parts may kill the plant prematurely or simply prevent it from growing in size and competing successfully with plants of other species.

High but sub-lethal intensities of grazing by vertebrate animals tend to produce distinct growth forms of heather which can be classified as 'carpet', 'topiary' and 'drumstick' (or 'mop') forms (see Figure 4.5). 'Carpet' heather can also be the result of severe weather conditions ('wind clipping') and can be found on exposed ridges and hill tops even where grazing pressure is low.

'Carpet' heather

A heather seedling develops a well-defined leading shoot from which lateral shoots also arise. The lowermost side-shoots develop strongly, producing a pyramidal growth form, and they may root where they make contact with the soil. If the shoot system above the lowermost side-shoots is destroyed by grazing or severe weather these shoots allow growth to continue and they may begin to grow upwards at the tips to form new leaders. If shoot destruction of this kind is recurrent a dense, mat-like growth form results.

'Topiary' heather

After a few years, the leading shoot of a heather seedling usually dies. Two or three new leading shoots develop in its place. This process continues and results in the development of a rounded bush. The lowermost lateral branches become a much less significant component of the structure than in younger plants. More intense destruction of shoot tips will further increase the number of growing points and the density of shoots in the canopy, although the growth in size of the bush may be considerably curtailed. In an isolated bush, heavy grazing will produce a dense compact canopy down to ground level.

'Drumstick' or 'mop' heather

When heather plants grow in a dense stand the lowermost lateral branches become shaded and die. Most of the remaining branches are more or less upright. A very intense but brief episode of damage by grazing, cutting or burning will quickly strip the canopy and promote the growth of new shoots from the stem bases, provided the stems are not too old. However, if canopy destruction is only partial, but prolonged, stem base buds which could produce new shoots may not be activated, growth of prostrate lateral branches will no longer be an option, and the growth of the remaining canopy will be constrained. This may be the origin of 'drumstick' or 'mop' heather bushes in which the heather canopy is reduced to small, compact masses of intertwined and contorted shoots on the ends of scattered long, bare stems.

(Source: MacDonald, 1990)

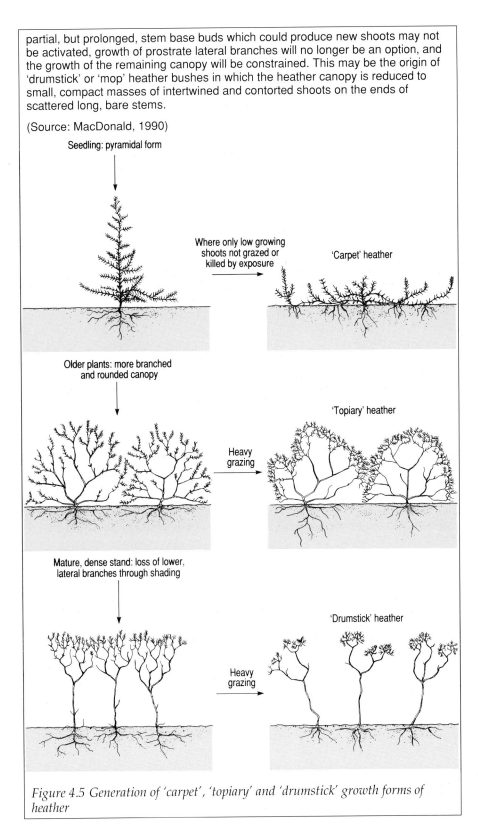

Figure 4.5 Generation of 'carpet', 'topiary' and 'drumstick' growth forms of heather

Regular burning can help to rejuvenate and maintain the heather stand but frequent, large-scale or careless burning in combination with a high grazing intensity can lead to the replacement of heather by other vegetation. Burning favours the heather species and other fire-resistant plants, whereas burning and grazing favour the species that are resistant to both activities. On wet ground heather can be replaced by purple moor-grass and cotton grass; on dry ground fescue and bent grasses may dominate the sward, while heavy grazing has the same effect anywhere.

Many grouse moors are drained with the aim of maintaining and encouraging the growth of heather. As heather does not thrive in wet boggy areas the object is to increase water run-off and lower the water table to improve the growth and cover of heather. However, evidence for improved heather growth after draining and consequent better performance by red grouse and sheep is limited.

Unlike partridges and pheasants, red grouse are not reared in captivity and later released to be harvested by shooting. Although grouse can easily be reared on a diet of commercial fowl food supplemented with heather, birds released from captivity cannot cope with the change in diet and often die or disappear. The best way of increasing numbers is good moorland management (see Chapter 5). Detailed research and advice on game management is provided by the Game Conservancy (see the *Helpful Organisations* booklet in the foundation module).

Value of grouse shooting

A well-managed grouse population can be considered a valuable asset and if run on a commercial basis can provide an acceptable financial return. A well-managed English moor of 1500 hectares will produce on average 1000 **brace** shot per annum. In Scotland there is a sporting rate which is based on average bag records over the previous years. The grouse stocks on most Scottish estates have diminished in recent years and, although less than 200 brace are shot each year on many moors, the owners must pay high sporting rates based on the previously high bag records. The result has been that numerous commercial estates are paying more in rates than they obtain from their clients in the same year, and consequently they have been forced to turn the land over to alternative uses. No rates are levied on these alternative land uses – forestry and re-seeding or other agricultural reclamation for intensified hill farming.

In the north of England the subsidies paid to hill farmers have encouraged an increased grazing intensity on heather ground, leading to a loss of heather and a decrease in grouse stocks. Once the valuable shooting rights are lost, land values fall and the only viable alternative on many moors is afforestation (see Box 4.2 in the foundation book).

Red deer

There is a large population of red deer in Great Britain, especially in the Scottish uplands. Although the vegetation is poor and the growing season is short, this primarily woodland animal can exist on moorland throughout the year. In the winter months they may attempt to seek refuge in forests and improved agricultural land where they can cause considerable damage. Nevertheless, red deer do have a good sporting value and increasingly are being farmed for venison.

Deer numbers

At present red deer numbers are limited by the overwintering ground available, not by the huge areas of their summer range. Their winter range, normally below the 450–500 metre contour, is the type of ground which attracts forestry and which hill farmers favour for improvement; deer stocking densities will vary according to the quality of such range available to them. On good wintering ground densities of 70 to 80 deer per 100 hectares have been encountered while on poor quality ground 20 to 30 deer per 100 hectares are more usual.

It is essential for red deer stocks to be reduced to compensate for any loss of winter range when it is fenced to exclude them from farming improvements or forestry. If not, natural mortality and out-of-season killing will inevitably rise, and damage that is unacceptable to neighbouring land users will occur.

Culling

In Scotland red deer have no natural predators. Without **culling**, quality and health would deteriorate because of overstocking and numbers would increase to the point where high natural mortality would occur. Shooting also enables landowners to make a necessary financial return towards the cost of management through selling venison or letting sporting rights.

It is important to cull female deer as well as males. There is no shortage of people willing to stalk and shoot red deer stags but hinds are less prized as a quarry. The result is that, on balance, there are too many hinds in most areas. Many owners believe that if hind stocks increase there will be more stags to stalk. This is not altogether correct because as the number of hinds increases, stags tend to be pushed off their grazing areas to the fringes of the forest where, in winter, they are shot illegally by poachers or legally as marauders on farms or in forests.

For humane reasons it is better for estates to control deer by shooting rather than to allow animals to die of starvation in the winter. Geographical and other circumstances can sometimes make it difficult for effective action to be taken by one estate on its own. Co-operation amongst estates is usually to their mutual benefit.

The aim of the land manager is to keep numbers of red deer to levels that will yield the most good quality deer, while at the same time minimising pressure and damage on neighbours' land. Once established, this balance can be maintained by an annual cull equal in number to each year's recruitment less natural losses. With an annual *survival* average of 33 calves per 100 hinds, the Red Deer Commission recommends that a cull of one-sixth of the mature animals, of each sex, will keep a population numerically stable. Selective culling at the correct intensity is an important means of improving breeding stock by weeding out old and unfit animals of all ages.

Deer stalking

Deer stalking provides an important sporting attraction on more marginal land in Scotland, where it can represent a valuable asset. Such land has, in recent years, had high capital values based on the average annual number of stags shot. The areas of land involved can be large, with deer numbers ranging from as many as one stag to every 50 hectares to as few as one stag to every 2500 hectares. Red deer stalking can be let by the day and the rent is charged per stag. A stalker, to track down the animals, is normally provided by the estate, together with a vehicle or pony and also accommodation on the more remote estates. The carcass remains the property of the estate.

Deer farming

Deer farming systems have increased in popularity over the past decade, particularly in upland areas. Most deer farms are producing venison either for farm-gate retail sale or for a wholesale market. Several farms also produce breeding stock for sale to other farmers at home and abroad, and for restocking natural herds.

Domestic demand for venison is fairly low, mainly due to irregular supply, and to the high cost compared to beef. However, the market is developing, with the recent consumer preference for leaner meat, and with exports to mainland Europe.

Deer can be farmed on most types of land, provided that some shelter is available in the form of natural vegetation or overwintering accommodation. However, the quality of grazing will influence the stocking rate, which in turn varies according to the intensity of management. On good quality land, 8 to 14 hinds per hectare should be achievable, whereas on marginal grazing land and in deer parks one to three hinds per hectare may be more appropriate. Secure deer fencing is essential. A perimeter fence should be 1.8 to 2 metres high, constructed of heavy quality woven wire and with posts 15 to 20 metres apart.

Amenity grassland

Amenity grasslands form a small but important proportion of Great Britain's land area (see Table 1.1). Nearly half of these grasslands are devoted to sporting and recreational activities that require an intensively managed grass sward, which is repeatedly cut short and suffers much trampling or heavy wear. They are obviously important landscape features, especially in urban and suburban areas, but their wildlife value is extremely limited. Of the other amenity grasslands, more than 120000 hectares consist of roads and railside verges (which are dealt with in *Practical Conservation: Boundary Habitats*); a similar area is in the form of commons in England and Wales with public access, while nature reserves and golf rough each take up about 60000 hectares. Country parks account for less than 20000 hectares.

Commons

Commons are areas of unenclosed land, privately or publicly owned, which are subject to rights held by other people – the commoners – such as grazing, pannage and estovers (see the *Legislation and Regulations* booklet in the foundation module). Many commons are the surviving remnants of the manorial waste and hill pastures of medieval times.

There are 600000 hectares of common land in England and Wales, if sites without public access are included, but this is a fraction compared to the area that existed before the enclosure movement of the 18th and 19th centuries. Nevertheless, since most commons have remained unploughed, they are rich in wildlife and archaeological sites. Traditional grazing and the existence of other rights have protected some commons from the intensive modern agricultural methods, but many have still suffered in conservation terms because of these rights both not being exercised and being overexercised. Commons are particularly rich in grassland, heath, moor and scrub habitats.

Commons are covered by many laws, but in particular where grazing or other rights exist then ministerial permission is required before carrying out works, such as fencing or constructing roads and buildings. While this gives some degree of protection from development it does place constraints on the management of the grazing.

Some commons are subject to management schemes under existing legislation or are owned and managed by public bodies for the primary objectives of conservation and access. Others have commoners' associations or management associations dealing with the exercise of rights and agricultural management. Many, however, have no provision for conservation management, nor for co-ordination of their varied uses.

There is a public right of access to about one-fifth of our common land. Despite customary use of much of the remainder, there is no legal right to be there, except along public rights of way.

There are over 2000 golf courses in Great Britain, occupying a significant amount of land. The first golf courses were developed in the 17th and 18th centuries on coastal dune systems, followed by the sandy inland heaths. In the 19th century parkland courses were built on fertile grassland surrounded by mature trees or woodland. Originally, the grassland of many golf courses was kept short by grazing sheep but this has given way to mechanical and sometimes chemical methods. Because of their origin as semi-natural habitats, the variety of habitat types involved (short grass, long grass, scrub, woodland and standing water), and the seclusion of and lack of interference in some parts, many golf courses are particularly rich wildlife sites. Some even have SSSIs or are a refuge for extremely rare and endangered plants and animals. New golf courses are still being built, particularly on arable land, which provides many opportunities for maintaining, enhancing and creating wildlife habitats.

As indicated above, golf courses consist of a variety of vegetation types that are subject to different types and intensity of management. The tees and greens are intensively managed, being mown very frequently (two to seven times per week) and subject to periodic use of fertiliser and pesticides. Consequently, the high quality turf is almost exclusively made up of grasses and supports very little wildlife. Fairways are less intensively managed, being mown normally on a weekly basis. This does allow a certain number of broad-leaved plants to grow, some of which (e.g. daisies) are unwanted. Spot-treatment with herbicide can control these problem plants without affecting more attractive species such as wild thyme, small cranesbill and clovers. Even so the wildlife value of fairways is limited.

Semi-rough consists of a strip of slightly longer grass, intermediate in height between the fairways and the true rough. Like the fairways, it is less intensively managed than the greens. Mowing on a fortnightly or monthly basis, and a lack of fertilisers and herbicides, allows many herbs to grow amongst the grass. Even more variety exists where the clippings are removed, as this helps herbs to become established. Removing the clippings also reduces the frequency of mowing as the sward grows more slowly. The rough, which can be one of various types of grassland or heath, is left almost undisturbed and in a natural state. Any management of the rough depends on the type of golf course, e.g. coastal links, parkland, heathland. Being undisturbed, rough can be invaded by scrub in as little as five years. This may be desirable in certain areas as a feature of the golf course but often it has to be controlled, particularly in its early stages of development.

Since the first country park was officially opened in 1970, there has been a rapid growth in this type of outdoor recreation facility. Some of these parks had for long been used by the public for recreation. Others were public open spaces to which there had been unlimited access for many years. In addition, many new parks have been created, both by local authorities and private concerns, either from land which was previously farmed or from areas such as disused gravel pits, old quarry workings and old brick-pits. Country parks vary considerable not only in size, facilities offered and types of vegetation present but also in the authority responsible for their administration. They range in size from under 10 hectares to over 1500 hectares, although the majority are below 100 hectares. Of the major vegetation types represented in country parks, grassland, of all types, is the most common, covering roughly 50% of the total area. Heath and grass-heath, often mixed with bracken and usually with some invasion by birch or pine, are also present in several country parks.

Country parks are usually situated within 40 kilometres of centres of population. Many are sited within city boundaries and there is now a trend to locate new country parks nearer the urban fringe than was the case with some of the earlier parks. They have proved very popular with the public, especially car-owning families who account for 80% of the visitors. Sundays and bank holidays attract the largest numbers, although the weather causes wide fluctuations in visitor numbers.

More than 80% of country parks are owned and/or managed by local authorities. Where a country park is not owned by the local authority the authority often has some form of management agreement with the owner, for example on some sites owned by the National Trust.

4.2   Integrating conservation and business interests

If the conservation and business aspects of grassland, heath and moor management are considered in isolation, they tend to become increasingly incompatible. On the other hand, if they are considered together there is much scope for supporting both aspects. Grasslands, heaths and moors are sustained by particular management practices. Changes in these practices inevitably lead to changes in the habitat which fall into two broad groups – an intensification of previous practice or a withdrawal or complete change in the previous practice or use of the land.

Intensification of agriculture

Traditional agricultural methods generally favoured the development and persistence of species-rich grassland. Technical innovations and economic incentives have both increased the intensity of management in most areas but reduced it in others, leading to an overall decline in conservation value. The area of land under cultivation and the proportion of arable to grazing land have been extended through ploughing old established grassland and 'reclaiming' semi-natural heath and downland. In addition, much research, advice and money have been directed towards improving the productivity of land under pasture. The average production of grass has increased significantly through the increased application of fertilisers and herbicides, greater use of drainage, and grass cultivars that are best suited to these conditions. This has led to increased stocking rates and grazing pressure and the production of silage rather than hay. All of these activities tend to reduce plant diversity and exclude rare species.

Withdrawal of agriculture

Not all marginal grasslands have undergone reclamation and intensification of agriculture. The management of some has not changed significantly whilst others have been subject to withdrawal of agriculture. Chalk

HEATHER? — NO, NO HEATHER HERE — ONLY DAISY, BUTTERCUP, BLUEBELL...

downland and certain areas of lowland grass heath fall into the latter category. The free-range system of grazing, especially by sheep, which for centuries helped to maintain the short, springy and herb-rich downland sward has almost completely disappeared and, while these grasslands may have escaped the plough and afforestation, the structure and composition of many of them has been completely changed by the withdrawal of grazing.

The effect of undergrazing on the composition of the grassland was enhanced by the arrival of the rabbit disease myxomatosis in 1954. This drastically reduced the rabbit population which had previously had a significant grazing effect. Marked changes in the structure and composition of many lowland grasslands date from that time. The removal of a more or less intensive grazing regime of stock and rabbits has had various effects. Selectively grazed species have tended to increase at the expense of those species requiring bare ground or short, open vegetation, such as the smaller, short-lived herbs. The sward becomes dominated by ranker and more aggressive grasses, so the plant-species diversity is reduced. However, the accumulated litter and greater number of flower and seed heads may support a greater diversity of insect life. The absence of grazing also means that succession is no longer prevented and woody species can invade and establish successfully.

Fluctuating red grouse populations and changing economic circumstances have also seriously affected heather moors which are managed for grouse shooting. Much of the value of these semi-natural habitats is lost by lack of management or deliberate conversion to improved grassland or forestry plantations.

Withdrawal of traditional management has often been most noticeable in the case of common land, where commoners have stopped exercising their rights to grazing due to economic reasons or a change in the socio-economic class of commoner, or increases in traffic where commons are bisected by busy roads. The reduced grazing has inevitably led to invasion by scrub and rank, unpalatable grasses which may favour bird species but not plants and insects. These problems are often compounded by a lack of a consistent mechanism for managing commons.

Management schemes

Only a small minority of commons have management associations or boards of conservators established under various Acts of Parliament. On most commons, no single party has taken a lead because of the number of interests in the common, or in some cases the lack of them. Many commons have no registered owner and although they have been placed in the care of the local authorities they have no power of management. Thus, with commons there is a need to set up management mechanisms before addressing the actual habitat management requirements.

Similar issues exist for some country parks. Attitudes to countryside recreation vary from authority to authority, some devoting considerable resources to country parks, others giving countryside recreation a low priority. Inevitably, the attitude adopted towards visitors, vegetation management and landscape and wildlife conservation by a local authority is strongly influenced not only by the finance available, but also by the composition of the committee responsible for these activities. In preparing management plans for habitats in country parks, it is important to remember that the principal function of the parks is to provide visitors with the opportunity of informal recreation in a countryside setting. They must be visually attractive and at the same time enable visitors to relax and pursue activities which they find enjoyable and satisfying. Wildlife may form an important component of visitor enjoyment, but country parks should not overstress nature conservation – nature reserves exist specifically to fulfil that function. However, management techniques should be used which are compatible with both people and wildlife.

Finance is an important constraint in selecting a management option, and with limited budgets and restrictions on increased expenditure, habitat management in country parks must be cheap and make the best use of existing resources. Agricultural activities, such as grazing and hay- and silage-making, provide both a valuable contribution towards reducing maintenance costs and an income in some country parks. Agricultural practices may need to be modified if they are to be compatible with recreation, but with careful planning, farming in country parks may add considerably to visitor enjoyment by creating a rural atmosphere which blends in with the surrounding landscape.

Reconciling business and conservation interests

Most agricultural improvements will conflict with the many non-agricultural values of grasslands. Reclamation of old pasture, drainage improvement, re-seeding, fertiliser application and herbicide treatment are aimed at securing a sward dominated by a few particularly productive and nutritious grasses and clovers. The best agricultural return is achieved from a green uniformity, whilst amenity and wildlife conservation value typically depend on a diversity of colour and form, such as is found in herb-rich pastures and meadows.

In general, conservation and agricultural value cannot both be maximised on the same piece of grassland. The greatest conservation interest will be achieved either where wildlife is the dominant land use, as in nature reserves, or where extensive farming systems can be economically sustained by agricultural or environmental grants. A reduction in the intensity of grazing and fertiliser and pesticide use can save on costs and still provide a reasonable return, but this will only lead to a slow and small benefit to wildlife. One other option is zoning of management. This can easily be done in country parks or on golf courses, where some areas can be intensively managed, while other, perhaps marginal, areas are not. It is also possible on field margins and boundaries (see *Practical Conservation: Boundary Habitats*) and may be possible for some fields on some farms.

An integrated assessment should therefore view the grassland, heath or moor areas in the context of the land holding as a whole, as described in the foundation book, and in relation to each other. At this stage it is important to consider land managers' objectives and the constraints under which they are operating. For the majority of holdings there will probably be a sole manager, although the wishes of family and friends and the views of a landlord or owner can be very important. However, many prime conservation areas will have management committees that need to place greater emphasis on resolving differences of opinion and taking up the opportunities provided. In either case, the construction of a management plan and an open-minded approach to the issues can help.

4.3   Making your own integrated assessment

Make an integrated assessment of the grassland, heath and moor in your own study area. It should include:

▶ a business assessment of the area, to take account of grass and animal production, game and amenity interests, as appropriate;

▶ a map that shows the relationship between the various uses of the land and the wildlife and landscape considerations;

▶ an indication of the perceived problems and opportunities and also past management practices, noting any existing or potential interactions between the management of the area for commercial and conservation purposes, making sure both negative and positive interactions are covered;

▶ an indication of the land manager's objectives and constraints.

The examples given in the next section for the case study areas should serve as a guide. With experience you will probably be able to assess the value of an area from both the commercial and the conservation points of view at the same time, and to summarise your integrated assessment on a single annotated map. Until you are familiar with the assessment process, however, it is advisable to do the assessments separately, step by step, to avoid overlooking anything.

4.4   Integrated assessment of case study areas

Borders hill farm

This is a tenanted, commercial hill sheep farm, running 1020 pure-bred Blackface ewes on the hill land and 40 suckler cows on the lower ground. The majority of the lambs are sold fat at local markets, some ewe hoggs being sold for breeding and others being used as replacements in the flock on the farm. The latter ensures that the flock remains immune to looping ill, a disease of sheep and grouse carried by a tick parasite which is present on the hill.

The sheep are 'hefted' (i.e. grazed on a particular section of the hill), feeding off the hill vegetation all year round – grasses mainly in the spring and summer and heaths in the late autumn and winter. With a stocking rate of approximately one ewe to 2.5 acres (1.0 ha) no additional feeding is necessary, except in periods of severe winter weather, when snow covers the heather and hay is fed to the sheep. 'Rumavit' protein feed blocks are located in each 'cut' (i.e. area of land between burns or streams) (see Figure 4.6). The position of these blocks remains the same throughout the year.

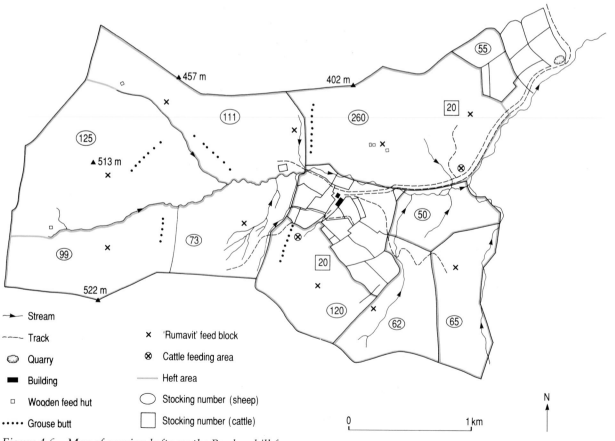

Figure 4.6 Map of grazing hefts on the Borders hill farm

They are used by the sheep as they 'rake' over the hill, i.e. as they come off the hill tops down to the glens and on their way back up to the hill tops in the evening. The 'Rumavit' blocks are necessary to increase the digestibility of certain plant material, especially heather, for sheep and cattle.

Cattle are grazed with the sheep on only two sites on the farm (see Figure 4.6). Both these areas are grass dominated by species that are common to poorer, more acid soils, e.g. fine bent, wavy hair-grass, purple moor-grass, sweet vernal-grass and mat grass. The majority of these grasses are highly seasonal in their palatability to livestock. However, cattle grazing aids the removal of the rougher grass herbage, encouraging a lower growing sward for sheep. This also allows sheep access to more nutritious shoots amongst the grass tussocks. The local saying 'the cattle make the sheep's meat' sums up this process. In the winter cattle receive additional feed of hay and straw from fixed feeding points.

Both the mixed grazing areas have variable degrees of heather cover, a clue to a more extensive cover in the past, which is verified by aerial photographs of the farm taken in 1946. Where the topography has allowed, these areas have received applications of lime in the past (i.e. pre-1976 under the lime subsidy). This, along with cattle grazing and possibly large or severe burns, will have shifted the vegetation balance more to grass species.

The majority of the **in-bye land** is under a grass rotation of two years rape/kale or turnips, followed in the second year by direct sowing into the crop of a hill grass–clover mix. This is grazed in its first year then possibly cropped for hay thereafter. Pastures receive lime, phosphate and potash applications with limited nitrogen to aid clover establishment. Weeds such as thistles and docks are chemically treated. Every year 10 hectares of grass are cut for hay. The remaining hay requirements are bought in.

Heather is therefore an important constituent in the winter diet of the sheep when grass growth is reduced. To ensure a high nutrient value in the heather, new growth must be stimulated by burning and grazing. To ensure that it regenerates well, and that the grazing pressure of the sheep is spread over the heft, burning should be on a fairly regular cycle (ideally when the heather is 20–30 centimetres tall or every 10 to 15 years) and in strips to build up a patchwork of heather ages.

At present burning of the moor is rather haphazard, being dictated by weather and available labour. Within the official burning season (1 October to 15 April) there are in practice approximately only 10 days in March/April that are suitable for burning. However, the poor spring weather over the last two or three years has severely limited the areas burned. With only a shepherd and an estate gamekeeper as full-time staff, additional casual labour has to be hired. This often causes problems, in ensuring a regular turn-out of people (ideally six) and payment (usually based on attendance on-site regardless of whether any burning is done).

This has often resulted in the employment of the minimum of labour, and therefore an increased chance of fires escaping, resulting in larger burns. Because of the proximity of the moor to forestry plantations, notification of burning must be given to the forestry owners in writing three weeks before burning and in the morning and evening of the day of burning. All such arrangements put stress on already stretched resources, i.e. the approaching lambing time for the shepherd and the main pest control period for the gamekeeper.

There is local evidence to suggest that bracken on the hill is increasing its cover and reducing the effective grazing area on the farm. This may have been aided by the larger-sized burn areas – bracken, with its underground **rhizomes**, is well adapted to colonise these areas. However, the cessation of cutting bracken for livestock bedding and the possible withdrawal of cattle from grazing on the open hill may also have allowed unrestricted growth of bracken. In addition to reducing the effective grazing area of the hill, bracken is also toxic to livestock, and the bracken litter harbours the early life stages of a tick which spreads looping ill disease amongst sheep and grouse. Control by cutting or chemical applications by tractor are limited by the accessibility of slopes to machinery, while the costs of chemical control by aerial application are often prohibitive. However, to minimise any impact of the chemical on other ferns in the gullies, on the SSSI semi-natural woodland area and on the water quality of the adjacent streams, the Nature Conservancy Council for Scotland (NCCS) and the local River Purification Board would have to be consulted before spraying.

Thirty bee-hives are located every summer and autumn in the valley bottom to utilise the meadow flowers and heather.

The shooting rights on the farm have remained with the owner. The heyday for grouse shooting appears from Figure 4.7 to have been between the wars with driven shoots and an average bag of 300 brace of grouse shot in a season. Today the lines of grouse butts around the farm are the only monument to these days.

The reasons for the decline in grouse numbers on the farm are many but typical throughout many moorland areas. First, the number of people employed in the rural landscape has decreased. During the inter-war years labour was readily available on the estate in the form of gardeners, maintenance staff, shepherds and gamekeepers for the heather burning and grouse beating.

In contrast, just after the Second World War, greater pressures on the land to produce the country's food needs resulted in a reduction of available labour on the land. The gamekeeper's time also became stretched between the grouse moor and managing a lowland pheasant shoot and the salmon fishing elsewhere on the estate. This reduced the labour available for tasks such as burning heather for grouse with the increased possibility of burns being lit and left or escaping, creating a large burn pattern.

At about the same time as the revolution in agriculture, a programme of steadily increasing afforestation was starting. Two adjacent hill farms were afforested over this period, effectively reducing the total extent of grouse moor in the area (although trees initially have a positive effect on grouse numbers until the closure of the canopy). The forestry is seen as a major cause of reduced grouse numbers on the moor because of the large numbers of pests, e.g. foxes and carrion crows, that it harbours. This was at a time when the gamekeeping on the farm was being effectively reduced because of other commitments.

Other factors such as disease amongst the grouse and indeed the attitude of the present owner, who has little personal interest in shooting, have led to the gradual reduction in grouse production on the farm.

The increasingly popular long-distance walk route at the southern boundary has caused occasional conflicts with the farming regime, such as when gates are left open. However, the risks in the future from increased numbers of

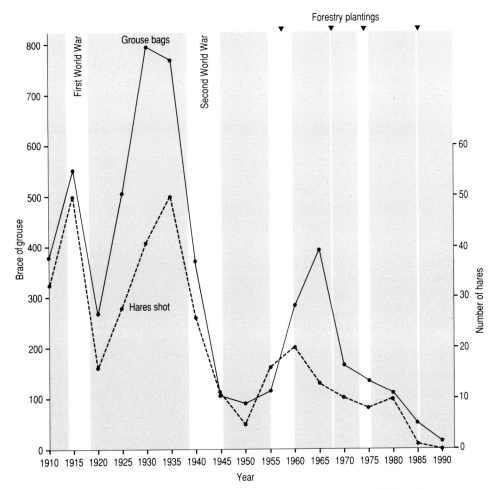

Figure 4.7   Average game bag records for hares and brace of grouse 1910–1990

walkers in the area may be more serious; for example, the potential fire risk to the heather, dogs chasing sheep and the destruction or sabotage of pest control devices such as traps for carrion crows, etc.

Stelling Minnis Common

An integrated assessment of Stelling Minnis Common needs to take account of the different users of the area and of the needs of the various interest groups. The present interests and uses can be summarised as follows.

1   The Commoners

The Stelling Minnis Commoners' Association has a constitution and looks after the interests of the registered commoners. At present up to 51 commoners' sheep are grazed, being turned out at 9 am and brought back at 4 pm each day (or sooner if it is dark or foggy); 14 commoners have paid £70 each to buy ewes with lambs and three commoners graze their own sheep, bringing the total to 60 animals.

With the present poor sheep prices, there is no return on the stock, and the commoners also have to pay vets' bills and £20 per year each for winter keep. Grazing is therefore a matter of principle – rights should be exercised and the common kept as it was traditionally.

2 The Conservators

The Conservators of Stelling Minnis are appointed by the Trustees to protect and preserve the Common and they are responsible for the day-to-day management of the area. This involves mostly mowing the open areas, and scrub clearance using a tractor and chain. A JCB is sometimes brought in to remove large stumps.

This work of 'tidying' the Common has been done largely without expert advice, and without any agreed formal management or conservation plan to date. Nor is it always appreciated, by either conservation or amenity interests. Although a blunt instrument, it has certainly been needed to maintain the Common in the absence of more widespread grazing.

3 The Friends

The Friends of Stelling Minnis raise money for the Conservators. There are 180 members who pay £1 per year each, and public events raise further sums of up to £2000 in some years. The Friends of Stelling Minnis gave a grant to the drawing up of a grazing plan for Stelling Minnis Common in 1985 which has not been implemented, and the money funds the maintenance of the Common (see point 2 above). The Friends of Stelling Minnis also provide some work parties to carry out projects detailed by the Conservators.

They have a useful role in involving and interesting people in the upkeep of the Common, and maintaining it as part of the local community.

4 Public users

Stelling Minnis Common is used frequently by visitors for informal recreation. Most people come by car; on a recent Bank Holiday Monday, 127 cars were counted. On average Sundays in summer, 100 to 120 people may be on the Common. Many of them picnic, walk short distances, play football or sit in or near their cars. Other users are horse-riders, walkers and cyclists. Many of these people are local residents, for example, walking their dogs.

The right to informal recreation is highly valued and makes the Common very special. It is not without its problems: for example, travellers recently pitched camp on the Common for the first time. They were successfully moved on by a court injunction within a week, and the incident showed how a watchful group like the Commoners' Association can act swiftly to protect an area. Even so, some people who value the area differently would like to see ditches dug to prevent all access, or for all management such as mowing to cease altogether. Many of these people are amongst the following groups.

5 Residents

The residents are as varied as the interests in the Common itself. The decline of grazing coincided with increased affluence and the growth of Stelling Minnis as a desirable place to live. When the last gate was removed in 1952 and grazing stopped, house fronts were often left unfenced. The recent grazing experiment, with sheep ranging freely, has met some adverse reaction from householders who find sheep on their lawns, but many residents have said that they like to see the animals back on the Common. Likewise, the feeling that the countryside should not be touched is well ingrained amongst many people who enjoy the wooded areas without realising or being concerned that the grass areas are declining.

The 'no intervention' lobby is thought to be declining as the need to manage the Common becomes more accepted, but it is still vocal, and a point of view that cannot be dismissed. Such views are often made known via the Parish Council.

6   Conservation

The value of the area for wildlife is unquestioned and well documented. What is crucial is the balance between the historic value of Stelling Minnis Common as open grazed heath, and its present interest as a mosaic of different habitats. Indeed, the KTNC wildlife management plan (also not widely accepted) proposes a policy of no further clearance of mature scrub and woodland. This approach may be too timid for some interests (such as those that would like to see grazing extended), and still too interventionist for the 'leave it alone' school!

The main management technique of mowing maintains the grass areas, but tends to create a more uniform and less rich habitat than grazing. Bracken is a particular problem. Cutting needs to be well timed and repeated and the material has to be removed; pulling it up by hand is time-consuming and probably ineffective; grazing (or rather trampling pressure) is not sufficient at present stocking rates. Herbicide use is an option, but may meet resistance from amenity interests.

7   The owner

The present owner is looking to support the proper management and use of the Common and to secure its future, and is co-operating with all interested bodies to produce a viable management plan with which all parties agree.

In order to develop a management plan that takes account of these many interests the Conservators were re-formed into a management committee of seven people, representing as many interests as possible. These new Managers of Stelling Minnis Common then arranged a meeting of people from the local community to discuss what needs to be done with the Common.

Two outcomes of this meeting were a brainstorming exercise (see Section 6.7 of the foundation book) to identify many possible options (see Figure 4.8 overleaf), and a preliminary objectives tree (see Section 4.7 of the foundation book) for the Managers to develop further in the subsequent months (see Figure 4.9 overleaf). At the time of writing, this exercise is still continuing. What is shown here is a first 'pass' through the management planning cycle with much iteration still to be done.

X Enclose village
   centre

? Access tracks
   be maintained

? Organise
   vermin control

✓ Remove roadside trees

✓ Move animals

? Leave sheep in
   village centre

X Farm 50% to
   raise money

✓ Cattle grids

? Electric barriers

? Use herbicides

X Car parking area

? No parking on
   common

X Turn into
   allotments

X Clear the lot

✓ Stock-proof fences
   for properties

? animal rate
  on access to property

✓ Boundary hedges

✓ Dogs on leads

Boundary
✓ ditches

✓ Clear ponds

✓ Warden for
   weekends

X Use less
   herbicides

? Ban dogs from
  common

✓ Unified working party

X Parish purchase
   Lord of Manorship

✓ Stop urbanisation

✓ Remove
  concrete drives

X Wheel-clamp
   Parkers

✓ Bring back
   Minnis sales

✓ More management
  people

✓ More work
  parties

? More
  mechanisation
  of management

? Give everyone
  rights to graze

? Temporary
  fencing

✓ Remove
  obstructions

Figure 4.8   Brainstorming exercise done by the Managers of Stelling Minnis Common about possible management options. (The ticked options were subsequently considered to be good ideas, those with a question mark as possibly good ideas, and those with a cross as bad ideas)

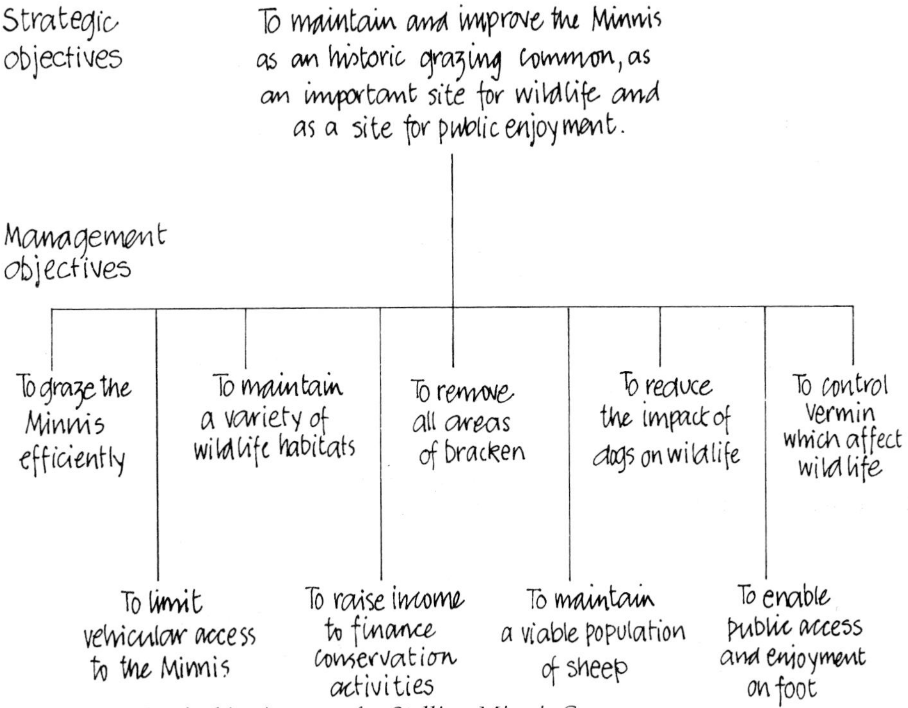

Strategic objectives

To maintain and improve the Minnis as an historic grazing common, as an important site for wildlife and as a site for public enjoyment.

Management objectives

To graze the Minnis efficiently

To maintain a variety of wildlife habitats

To remove all areas of bracken

To reduce the impact of dogs on wildlife

To control vermin which affect wildlife

To limit vehicular access to the Minnis

To raise income to finance conservation activities

To maintain a viable population of sheep

To enable public access and enjoyment on foot

Figure 4.9   Draft objectives tree for Stelling Minnis Common

Chapter 5

MAINTAINING AND IMPROVING EXISTING GRASSLANDS, HEATHS AND MOORS

The first stage of a full management planning exercise involves finding out 'where you are now' by making an integrated assessment of your local area, as described in Chapters 2, 3 and 4. This leads on to a consideration of 'where you would like to be' – exploring the strategic, management and tactical objectives for the land area as a whole – as described in the foundation book and as illustrated briefly in the case studies at the end of Chapter 4. This chapter concerns the next stage – the range of options available to put your objectives into practice.

When conservation is one of the objectives of grassland, heath and moor management, the appropriate options will depend on the site's present landscape and wildlife quality, and how they interact with the business aspects, i.e. the information collected for your integrated assessment.

Appropriate management options fall into three categories:

1   *maintaining* an area in its present form because it is a valued landscape feature or because it is a rare ecological type or contains rare plants and/or animals;

2   *improving* an area of moderate or poor conservation value, by changing its visual appearance or by increasing the overall ecological diversity and/or encouraging particular wildlife species;

3   *creating* new areas designed to support and encourage a wide diversity of wildlife and/or particular wildlife species.

This chapter concentrates on the first two categories, looking at conservation within existing grassland, heath and moor that already has some conservation value. The increasing rarity, vulnerability and length of time that it has taken to create such areas gives them a very high priority in any plan. The next chapter looks at the creation of new wildlife areas on arable land and the restoration or re-creation of wildlife habitats from intensively managed grassland. Although many of the considerations are the same as for existing good sites, the ability to design for specific objectives is greater on a 'green field' site, notwithstanding the greater task involved in producing a valued habitat.

As grasslands, heaths and moors are the product of the management regime that created them, maintenance of good habitats means maintaining sympathetic management practices which fall into three categories – grazing, cutting and burning – and avoiding damaging practices, such as ploughing, re-seeding, using fertilisers and pesticides, and drainage schemes. Improving poorer areas may also require the discontinuation of damaging practices and the establishment of 'traditional' practices, but this does not guarantee that a good habitat will result. Novel practices may be essential to achieve this. Indeed, each practice has to be applied carefully to achieve desired ends, while the scope for implementation is greater in extensive grazing lands than in intensively farmed areas.

5.1   Management practices

Grazing

The relationship between grazing animals and plant communities, and through them other members of the animal community, is complex. There is variation in the vegetation because of not only the climate, soil type and topography but also the type of grazing animals, how many there are and at what time of the year they are grazing. Nevertheless, there are many aspects which are understood. Grazing, for instance, has three main effects on vegetation: the sward is defoliated, plant life suffers physical damage by trampling, and nutrients are removed from or returned to the ecosystem.

The selection of certain plant species by livestock and the avoidance of others is an important factor determining the structure and composition of the vegetation. In general, animals select leaf material rather than stems, and prefer green and young material to dry and old material. Not surprisingly such selected material is easier to ingest and usually contains higher levels of digestible nutrients than unselected food. At the same time plant species preferences change throughout the year in response to the natural developmental changes in the plant community as different species flower. For instance, hill sheep in one area mostly ate red fescue throughout the year, but less so in May and June when there was new growth available from purple moor-grass, mat grass and sedges, and similarly from November to February when heather became important in the diet as other species became less accessible.

Defoliation

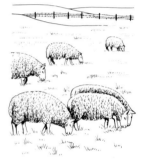

The stocking rate determines the level of selectivity of the grazing animal. At low stocking rates, livestock tend to select young, green plants, avoiding the rank ones. This increases the opportunity for change in the vegetation. In contrast, at high stocking rates, there is less herbage available per animal and they are forced to be less selective and eat the coarser, competitive grasses, thereby controlling them.

Summer grazing can affect the ability of plants to complete their flowering and seed setting. So, regular summer grazing may reduce the number of annual plants. This also affects many insects, most noticeably butterflies, which live and feed on flowers and seed heads. Autumn or winter grazing, or rotational grazing, is of most benefit to insects.

Trampling by livestock can affect both the structure and the composition of the plant community. It creates bare soil in the sward which allows the establishment of annual and perennial plants from seed, and it is also essential for the life cycle of many insects and other invertebrates. However, the degree of trampling depends on the stocking density and the soil type. The wetness of the soil determines how much it is cut up or poached. Excessive **poaching** of wet soils can lead to soil erosion, particularly on slopes, which reduces the opportunity for plant colonisation. Excessive trampling will also occur at specific points – for example, around gateways and water and feeding troughs or places – and lead to colonisation by plants that are adapted to such conditions. This can be a particular problem on heather moorland, where feeding areas should be regularly changed to avoid excessive trampling, which usually leads to a decline in the heather cover.

Trampling

Grazing animals help in the cycling of nutrients in an ecosystem through their dung and urine. Although this does not add nutrients to the ecosystem,

Nutrients

as does applying manure or artificial fertilisers, the pattern of dunging and urination in a pasture can have an important effect on the redistribution of nutrients. Areas that have received dung or urine are invariably avoided by grazing livestock for periods ranging from 4 weeks to 18 months. This results in a patchy appearance to the vegetation, except on areas that have constantly high stocking rates.

How a grazing animal bites the sward has a considerable effect on the structure of grassland, heath and moor. Sheep move slowly over the pasture and take successive bites close to the ground, leaving a fairly uniform, short sward. Cattle follow a similar pattern but curl their tongues around a tuft of vegetation and tear the plant tissue from the sward, often with a jerking movement. This creates a pasture with a mosaic of taller tufts interspersed with shorter vegetation. Horses and deer are 'close biters' but they are highly selective, so that a varied sward also results. However, selecting which type of livestock to use depends on many factors (see Table 5.1).

Cattle

Cattle can use a wide range of vegetation, both grassland and heath. They are not the most suitable grazing animals for steep slopes as they can cause erosion, and on wet ground or heavy clays there is a danger of poaching if grazing is allowed at the wrong time. Dairy cattle, because they need a high level of nutrition for maximum milk production, are less suited to many sites where conservation is an important aim unless stocking densities are low. The special facilities required for milking or winter housing also make them unsuitable for nature reserves or country parks where farming is not the prime concern. Rearing bullocks and heifers for beef production is better in these situations and for more extensive farming systems. Most breeds of cattle are docile, and generally require less looking after than other types of livestock. They rarely suffer injury from dogs, which is especially useful for sites which have public access or are close to large population centres.

Sheep

Sheep are the traditional grazing animal of herb-rich chalk downland. But they are also used extensively on open moorland. There are many breeds of sheep in Great Britain that are suited to different climates and different grazing conditions. In general they fall into two broad groups – hill and upland sheep, and lowland breeds. However, this distinction is not clear-cut as sheep have always been moved from upland to lowland areas and there has been a more widespread movement of different breeds in recent decades. Some hardy upland breeds are used in the lowlands, especially on nature reserves, country parks or exposed sites. However, upland sheep are most suited to extreme conditions of cold and wet and require large areas for successful management.

Unimproved, lush lowland pasture can support up to eight sheep per hectare, chalk grassland two sheep per hectare and moorland about one sheep per hectare, continuously grazing through the year. Higher densities are possible if all the land is grazed for part of the year only, or if parts of the land are grazed for short periods through rotational grazing, both methods producing the same average density. Both grassland and heath benefit from rotational systems (see below).

For non-agricultural areas breeding flocks of sheep are not recommended. Their management requires skilled labour and they are particularly demanding during lambing, shearing and dipping. Furthermore, pregnant ewes require additional feed during winter months to avoid mortalities and still births. Sheep are not suitable at all where access or proximity to high

Table 5.1 Summary of the factors for consideration in selecting a management technique for lowland grassland and heathland in country parks and similar areas

Type of management	Advantages	Disadvantages	Situation when appropriate
1 Grazing	(i) Attractive feature in country parks. (ii) Potential source of income. (iii) Saves cost cutting. (iv) Can be used on steep slopes where cutting is impossible.	(i) Requires experienced labour, fencing, additional machinery, etc. (ii) Potential risk of stock fatalities (litter and dogs). (iii) Livestock might create unpleasant mud, smell, flies, etc.	(i) Grassland with water and fencing and where visitor pressure is not too great nor is there a dog problem.
(a) Sheep	(i) Maintain floristic diversity. (ii) Safe with people. (iii) Traditional animal on certain grassland types. (iv) Saleable products – animals, carcass, wool. (v) Attractive feature of interest for visitor, especially lambs.	(i) Susceptible to dog worrying. (ii) High level of husbandry required, especially when breeding. (iii) Disease-prone on wet, poorly drained areas. (iv) Unsuitable on very productive grass swards over 10 cm.	(i) Chalk, limestone grassland, especially steep slopes. (ii) As component of mixed grazing on meadow, parkland, rough grazing. (iii) Low-medium public use, or intermittently on high public use areas when alternative grazing is available. (iv) Ancient earthworks and hill forts, etc.
(b) Cattle	(i) Maintain floristic diversity (ii) Safe with people. (iii) Not susceptible to dog worrying (excluding calves). (iv) Saleable products – animals, carcass, hides. (v) Attractive, moving feature in landscape. (vi) Certain breeds are ideal for reclaiming rough pasture.	(i) Calves susceptible to dog worrying. (ii) Minority of public may be scared by their 'inquisitive' behaviour. (iii) Can cause erosion on steep slopes. (iv) Can poach grass in wet weather. (v) Can damage cars.	(i) Chalk/limestone grassland not steep slopes. (ii) Meadowland (iii) Parkland (iv) Control of long coarse grass. (v) Reclamation management.
(c) Deer	(i) Exceptionally attractive feature in country parks. (ii) Very hardy, requiring minimum maintenance. (iii) Saleable products – venison, hides, antlers. (iv) Less susceptible to dog worrying.	(i) Very high costs involved in erecting and maintaining deer fence. (ii) Requires specialised labour with knowledge of deer husbandry. (iii) Tends to reduce floristic diversity. (iv) Stags are potentially dangerous in latter stages of rut.	(i) Established parkland with deer fence.
(d) Horse	(i) Attractive feature in parks. (ii) May be used for rides for public which can bring in revenue.	(i) Temperamental behaviour, especially if annoyed – may kick or bite. (ii) Very selective grazer, can spoil the floristic composition of sward – behavioural habits associated with dunging. (iii) High initial expense.	(i) Confined to paddock with public/horse interface at fence. (ii) Larger open areas where they can retire away from public.

Table 5.1 (continued)

Type of management	Advantages	Disadvantages	Situation when appropriate
2 Cutting	(i) Eliminates costs of fencing. (ii) Potential saleable product/rent from cutting rights. (iii) Can be used at all intensities of public use. (iv) No dog worrying. (v) No dung, smell, flies. (vi) Management has control over the type of finish on the grass, time and frequency of cut.	(i) Costs money to purchase, run, maintain and repair machinery. (ii) Can create a rather uniform and uninteresting landscape, more typical of recreation grounds. (iii) Cannot be easily used on steep slopes. (iv) Advantages of livestock foregone. (v) Labour on cutting could be more profitably used elsewhere.	(i) Situations when livestock requirements cannot be provided, or when public pressure is too high for livestock. (ii) Games and certain picnic areas. (iii) Formal areas.
(a) Gang mowing	(i) Can cover large areas quickly. (ii) Leaves ideal finish for sports areas, etc.	(i) No income can be generated, only costs incurred. (ii) Creates uniform and uninteresting sward. (iii) Need to cut regularly – gang mowers cannot cope with long grass. (iv) May produce undesired 'town park' appearance in country parks. (v) Clippings left on ground. (vi) Ground must be fairly level.	(i) Games areas and certain picnic areas. (ii) Areas of high public pressure.
(b) Flail, rear mounted and rotary cutters	(i) Can maintain large areas of grass in once/twice year cuts. (ii) Can cope with long coarse grass or scrub. (ii) Versatile – can be readily adjusted.	(i) No income generated. (ii) Clippings left on ground. (iii) Can leave uniform and uninteresting appearance to park.	(i) Topping grass swards. (ii) Forestry rides. (iii) Light/medium scrub control. (iv) Sports grounds.
(c) Hand-operated machines	(i) Can be used in places where tractor-powered machinery is unsuitable.	(i) Small rates of cut. (ii) High labour requirement.	(i) On slopes – small areas. (ii) Surrounding trees, car parks, etc. (iii) Formal areas.
(i) Cylinder mowers (ii) Rotary mowers (iii) Flymos (iv) Portable bush saws			(i) Formal gardens, flower beds, bowling greens, etc. (ii) Areas surrounding trees, car parks, small picnic areas, etc. (iii) Grass banks. Areas around trees, car parks, etc. (iv) Clearing scrub from steep slopes.
3 Agricultural cutting machinery – operated by farmers or as part of country park's own management programme	(i) Reduces costs of grassland maintenance. (ii) May provide income – sale/rent. (ii) Feed value of grass can be used instead of wasted.	(i) Lack of precise management control. (ii) May have to leave grass longer than otherwise, e.g. if using maintenance equipment.	(i) Large areas of grassland at present cut by maintenance machinery. (ii) Management can use/sell the product. (iii) Suitable farmers willing to operate own machinery.

Table 5.1 (continued)

Type of management	Advantages	Disadvantages	Situation when appropriate
(a) Hay-making equipment, cutter bar, tedder, baler – plus carting bales.	(i) Traditional technique may be vital for maintaining floristic interest of sward.	(i) Bales may be knifed by visitors if left around too long.	(i) Fairly highly productive grass – low intensity of public use.
(b) Forage harvester	(i) Can be used more regularly, e.g. every 6 weeks in growing season.		(i) All types of grassland on a terrain suitable for the machinery.
4 Burning	(i) Cheap. (ii) Used when grazing and cutting are both unfeasible. Traditional method for maintaining heathland, and certain grassland areas. (iii) Regeneration after fire may favour potentially undesirable species, e.g. bracken, purple moor-grass. (iv) Controlled burning may reduce risk of accidental burning, e.g. bracken.	(i) Potentially dangerous if out of control. (ii) Temporarily unattractive feature on landscape. (iii) Control of bracken litter. (iv) Limited period of year when safe or useful (February–March).	(i) Steep, unfenced grassland where grazing/cutting impractical. (ii) Regeneration of old stands of heathland.

(Source: Lowday and Wells, 1977)

population centres leads to a risk of worrying by dogs. All dogs can chase sheep, causing injury or death.

Horses and ponies

Horses and ponies tend to be highly selective, patchy grazers. This results in patches of coarse grassland interspersed with overgrazed areas. They also tend to defecate and urinate in the same area which can cause localised high nutrient levels. As well as overgrazing some areas horses will also poach the overgrazed ground or the ground around winter feeding sites, but not to the same extent as cattle. A low stocking rate equivalent to half to one animal per hectare is necessary to avoid these problems. Horses usually require considerable care during the winter months and can be expensive to feed, although hardy native ponies require little attention. Another problem on sites with access is the unpredictable temperament of horses and ponies, especially when confined to a paddock. They are therefore not suitable where there will be many visitors unless they are well fenced off.

Deer

Deer are becoming important livestock animals (see Chapter 4) but the effects of their grazing on natural vegetation and the composition of the plant community are poorly understood, either under the extensive grazing on the uplands or the more intensive grazing on deer parks and farms. Stocking rates vary from half to two red or fallow deer per hectare, depending on the quality of the grazing.

Goats

Goats will eat anything – including the toughest scrub. They are not widely kept because it is difficult to contain them unless they are tethered. However, rotational tethering will create a diverse structured sward that can also include scrub.

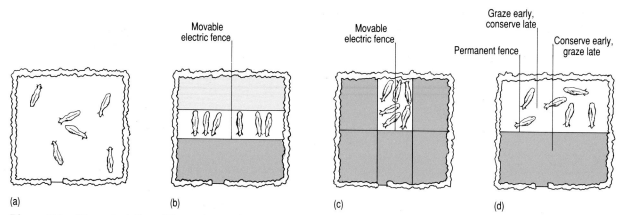

Figure 5.1   Characteristics of the main grazing systems: (a) continuous stocking; (b) strip grazing; (c) rotational stocking; (d) seasonal grazing or integrated grazing and conservation

Grazing systems

The impact of grazing depends not only on the types of grazing animals involved but also on the numbers involved and the times of year when they are grazing. Grazing systems fall into four broad categories – continuous stocking, rotational stocking, seasonal grazing and opportunistic grazing by one type of livestock – with the extra dimension of mixed grazing and integrating grazing and grass conservation (hay- or silage-making).

Continuous grazing

Continuous grazing involves keeping animals on one area of land for the whole of the grazing season (see Figure 5.1). The use of a low stocking density under a continuous grazing system maintains a mixture of short and long turf that contains many flowers and supports many insects, especially butterflies. Higher stocking rates reduce the diversity of height and structure in the vegetation. The resulting short turf contains fewer flowers and supports fewer insects, although a short turf is favoured by some butterflies. In all cases the impact of stocking density needs to be monitored and adjusted downwards if damage is suspected. Continuous grazing is most suitable on large areas where labour is scarce and fencing is limited or unavailable, or on tiny isolated sites where again it is difficult to maintain one of the other systems.

Rotational stocking

In rotational stocking, also known as paddock grazing, the site is temporarily or permanently divided up into compartments or paddocks with the grazing animals moved between them in a planned programme. (A variant of this is strip grazing where a fresh area of grass is provided each day by moving an electric fence, with a back fence used to stop overgrazing.) The resulting variation in sward heights is good for both flowers and insects. The size of the compartment depends on the size of the site, the availability of labour for moving stock and the costs of providing and maintaining fencing. Under intensive grazing systems (which do little for wildlife) as few as four compartments are used, each is grazed for one week and rested for three weeks, although the length of time is also determined by the amount of herbage present, the stocking rate and the size of the compartment. Under extensive systems, a diversity of sward heights can be created by using more compartments at a lower stocking density, although the size of compartment can be the same as in intensive systems, ranging from 0.5 hectares to more than 5 hectares. Electrified wire is often the simplest means of dividing a site into compartments and it is quick to erect and unobtrusive where aesthetic considerations apply.

The timing of grazing is important for many insects. Winter grazing (October to March) is generally considered to be least damaging as it is the time of year when invertebrates are dormant or relatively inactive. Summer grazing not only directly removes invertebrates and their feeding and breeding sites but also reduces the number of flowers. Nevertheless, the differing requirements of some butterflies mean that a mosaic of turf heights will nearly always be needed to maximise the number of species, otherwise one or more could be eliminated. Winter grazing may be sufficient where the turf is short and fine grasses predominate but, if there is an abundance of coarse grasses, additional light grazing may be necessary in some years or even every year to check the spring/early summer growth.

Opportunistic grazing is the use of grazing on an *ad hoc* basis whenever it becomes available or can be arranged. It may, for example, be used as a way of controlling coarse grasses in country parks where livestock is not usually kept. However, the stocking density and the proportion of the site grazed still need to be carefully considered because extensive damage, especially to butterflies, can occur if all the site is overgrazed.

Mixed grazing, particularly by sheep and cattle, is an effective way of producing a fairly uniform, close-cropped sward. Although cattle and sheep can be grazed together, often it is better to graze cattle first in the winter and spring, followed by sheep in the spring and summer.

Cutting

The cutting of vegetation, whether grassland, heather, bracken or areas of scrub, is widely practised. Variation in cutting techniques can directly encourage wildlife, although in many instances it is second best to grazing as a management technique.

The effects of cutting grassland are much more predictable than grazing but cutting tends to produce a uniform appearance and height to the sward. It is non-selective compared to grazing in that all the vegetation above the level of the cutting blade is severed, although the height and timing of any cutting imposes its own selection pressure. Grasses are likely to be favoured by frequent cutting, producing tillers freely under these conditions, in contrast to most broad-leaved plants which depend on regular seed production for survival and spread and produce vegetative parts less readily. Cutting allows the option of removing nutrients in the form of hay or silage, or returning them in part as clippings. On productive grasslands it is best to remove the cut grass and use it as fodder. On grasslands of low productivity which are not fertilised, it is not always necessary to remove cut material as long as it is shredded and evenly distributed in a fairly divided form to avoid smothering plants beneath. Cutting and returning the plant material to the same area of ground causes no long-term change in the nutrient status of the sward, the nutrients being recycled but not augmented. However, removal of cuttings does help increase plant diversity on very *fertile* sites.

As well as its effect on plant species, mowing grasslands can also have a dramatic impact on animals, especially insects and ground-nesting birds early in the summer. On a neutral grassland site a single cut in June can virtually wipe out a rich butterfly fauna. There is a sudden loss of shelter and of the parts of plants used by larvae for feeding and by pupae for resting; a severe reduction in nectar sources for adults; and a loss of territory markers, courtship posts and roosting sites. There is also the direct impact that the machinery can have on all stages of an insect's life cycle, and on structures such as anthills on chalk grassland.

Flail mowers can be used on scrub plants, to trim both desirable shrubs like heather and undesirable ones like bracken, bramble, hawthorn, birch and pine scrub. The aim in the first case is to stimulate regeneration of heather that has become overmature; the aim in the second case is to weaken or eliminate scrub invasion and/or the shading out of the grassland sward. The effectiveness depends on the age of the shrub plants, the frequency of cutting and the use of complementary techniques such as grazing, burning and herbicide treatments. On smaller areas hand-held tools may be used for controlling scrub if labour is not scarce.

Burning

The use of fire as a method of controlling vegetation is a simple concept, but the actual use or effects of burning are complex. Two important aspects are the amount of heat generated in different parts of a habitat and the timing of the burn. The amount of heat generated during a fire will depend on the weather conditions before and during the fire, on the topography of the site and on the quality, quantity and disposition of the fuel. Moisture in the soil facilitates conduction of heat into the soil while in a dry soil higher surface temperatures are likely because there is little downward conduction of heat. Wind speed is important as it can both have a cooling effect and increase the oxygen supply, thereby increasing the rate of combustion. Fire moves faster uphill than on level ground, and slower downhill. For example, fires spread twice as quickly up a 10 degree slope than on level ground. On very steep slopes, fire may spread as much as 65 kilometres in an hour. Doubling the amount of combustible material per unit area doubles the rate of spread and increases the height of flames. Back fires (those moving against the wind) are hotter than head fires (those moving with the wind), the highest temperatures being nearer the ground.

The effect of fire on habitats is not uniform. The extent of damage to the habitat and to the plant species present will depend to a greater or lesser extent on the time of year, the stage of development of the plants, the temperature of the fire and the sensitivity of the species to fire. Fire will cause a change in the vegetation, especially if the frequency of fires is increased. It also alters soil properties after burning, increasing soil temperatures during the day in the absence of vegetation, and lowering them at night.

If the above-ground temperature is not too high then many plants will regenerate from below-ground buds although the parts above ground are destroyed. Similarly, many seeds can survive controlled burns. Burning is restricted by law to certain times of the year (see Sections 5.2 and 5.3) when temperatures are less likely to be damaging. For instance, temperatures above 500 °C for more than one minute at the base of the stem will kill any heather plant, irrespective of age; while temperatures above 200 °C are normally lethal to heather seeds on the soil surface (although heat treatment for up to one minute actually stimulates germination). Such temperatures are normally only reached in very hot or uncontrolled fires in old stands of heather or during drought conditions. Severe burning or repeated burning will affect the relative proportion and dominance of species in grassland or heath because heather has to regenerate from buried seed while the increased bare ground enables annual and biennial plants to establish or bracken to regenerate more quickly. Burning is also highly damaging to most invertebrates that live above ground, and their survival depends on only part of a site being burned in any one year to enable recolonisation of the burned area. Burning can be very effective in removing rank grass and litter. It is a natural factor in many grasslands worldwide and can be the cheapest management option.

Herbicides may be used to control unwanted plants, such as bracken, either to kill them or to prevent regeneration after cutting. They should be used with care, since herbicides, whether broad spectrum or selective, change the plant community if used widely. They reduce plant species numbers, particularly broad-leaved species, but not usually the height of the vegetation.

Growth regulators are sometimes used to restrict the growth of vegetation in specific areas, such as roadside verges. Although they do not kill plants directly they strongly retard or prevent the flowering of grasses and so bring about substantial long-term changes in species composition.

5.2   Management strategies

It is important to know how different management *practices* operate, and their effects on the vegetation and other wildlife. But, in deciding on an appropriate management *strategy* for a particular site, these practices have to be deployed in a variety of ways to meet the objectives of the land manager; whether that is resolving conflicts between commercial and conservation interests, or deciding to encourage particular types of wildlife – birds and butterflies for instance – more than others. In this respect the different needs of different organisms have to be considered. As discussed in Chapter 3, three main factors determine the ability of a grassland sward to support a wide range of wildflowers, to harbour a diverse range of insects and to provide appropriate habitats for birds.

The first factor is the nutrient status of the soil which mostly influences plants. The second factor is the micro-structure of the vegetation – the number of vegetation layers, the density of the grass sward and its height (including bare patches of soil) – which is important for the continued survival of many plants and insects. Thirdly, there is the diversity provided by the macro-structure of the site which includes both larger vegetation in the form of scrub, hedgerows or trees and the topography of the land. This macro-structure is of value to plants, insects and birds, the latter often needing different feeding, nesting and roosting sites in the same area.

Lowland grasslands

Some sites maintain a natural mosaic of sward heights with high plant and animal diversities without any need for management for many years. This tends to occur on sites with predominantly thin and patchy soils where climate stress and/or rabbit grazing are important factors. Disused quarries, derelict industrial sites and very steep slopes may all develop in this way and can largely be left alone (although scrub invasion can eventually take over). However, the majority of good sites depend on, or result from, some form of regular management.

The short, fine, herb-rich swards of chalk downland with its attendant insects largely result from very specific grazing regimes. Winter grazing by sheep, preferably in selected parts of the habitat, is the best option to maintain this habitat type although it tends to encourage scrub development. Other animals may produce the desired results but their heavier weight, particularly on slopes, necessitates low stocking densities. Some spring grazing may be needed if there are coarse grasses present, and if there is no resident rabbit population. Mowing is a poor alternative and must be selectively done, especially where butterflies are present. Trial sections cut at different times of the year should be tried before being used more extensively. Invading scrub needs to be dealt with separately (see below).

Neutral and acid pastures

The options for managing neutral and acid pastures are as numerous as the types of pasture and land managers' objectives. Where stocking density is low then either a continuous or a rotational system will benefit both plants and animals. Under larger stocking densities an extended rotational system will enable plants to flourish, but may not be as favourable to animals if all areas end up being heavily grazed, even for a short time. Alternatively, an area can be grazed in the winter but left to grow as a hay crop in the summer, but this still favours wildflowers more than animals.

A problem with some pastures is the presence or invasion of perennial weed species such as thistles, nettles and docks. These can be controlled with minimum harm to other wildlife by selective application of a herbicide using spot-treatment with a knapsack sprayer or a weed wiper, or by mowing them off at a height of about 15 centimetres before they flower and set seed. Repeated treatments every year will eventually eliminate perennial weeds.

Particular care is also needed in damp or boggy grassland. Heavy winter grazing by larger livestock will probably result in excessive damage from trampling, but sheep are not usually grazed on wet lowland areas because of the dangers of the liverfluke parasite. Light grazing by a low density of cattle is therefore best.

Hay meadows

Meadows are usually cut for hay production, often in the spring and again once, twice or even three times later in the season. This provides good conditions for wildflowers but does not produce the variety of sward heights required by insects.

Amenity grassland

The management options for amenity grasslands are much wider than those for agricultural grasslands, as several techniques can be used on the same site to achieve a variety of objectives. For conservation purposes, the main aim should be to provide a mosaic of vegetation types to enable the widest possible diversity of plants and animals, while providing as many opportunities as possible for informal and formal, active and inactive recreational pursuits. The full range of factors that need to be considered are summarised in Table 5.1.

Lowland heaths

All management options for heaths should be aimed at creating a varied mosaic of vegetation with heather of varying ages. It is also important to maintain a certain amount of bare sandy ground (not more than 20% of the area), this being a particularly important feature for many animals, as well as stands of shrubs such as gorse and scrub birch. However, the amount of bracken should be minimised, which often means preventing the heather stands reaching the degenerate phase, when invasion by grass and shrub species is likely to be greatest.

Good heathland sites can be grazed by cattle, sheep or both, to maintain self-generating heather stands. Cattle are particularly good at suppressing bracken (and heather) by trampling and sheep control grass and tree invasion by grazing. Basal regeneration of young heather stands is also possible with grazing. Degenerate, weed-invaded heaths need more drastic treatment to regenerate the heather from seed (see also Chapter 6).

The greatest diversity of plants and animals are found in the mature phase and therefore only a small proportion of old heather should be managed in any one year, either to create bare ground or to promote new growth of heather for the future. Although burning is a traditional management technique for maintaining heaths it is difficult to control on smaller sites or if the vegetation has become dense. Nevertheless, many heaths, especially those near to urban areas, often suffer accidental (or malicious) fires with sufficient regularity to warrant additional management action. The objective is then to prevent fire claiming the majority of the heath and seriously damaging the invertebrate fauna.

The main alternative is to flail the heather and, where restoration is important, to 'rotovate' (i.e. use a rotary cultivator) the ground (see Chapter 6). Flailing should always be done in winter to avoid damage by machinery to other plants and animals. It is not usually necessary to remove the cut vegetation unless it is very thick, in which case a forage harvester or equivalent may be needed on large areas, or removal by hand on smaller areas. An alternative may be to gather the cut material together and burn it, as the spot used will then create a patch of bare ground. Rotovating can produce a good mixture of bare ground and heather stands but the sand may need to be recompacted to some extent and protected from erosion (see Chapter 6). Possible management programmes are outlined in Table 5.2.

Bracken and scrub should be restricted to areas near the edge (or verge) of the heath and should be controlled as soon as it starts to invade the heath. Pulling up or trampling young bracken fronds on burnt or rotovated areas can reduce encroachment, but is labour intensive. The alternative is to use a selective herbicide like 'Asulam'. Small clumps of mature gorse and broom and scattered bushes of birch, aspen and sallows may be retained for conservation purposes but otherwise these species, pine trees and rhododendrons should be eliminated by cutting down and chemically treating the stumps with selective herbicide to prevent regeneration.

Upland moorlands

Upland moorland normally consists of a mosaic of grass-dominant communities, heather-dominant communities and blanket bog. On grouse moors rotational burning is used to maintain young stands of heather on which grouse can feed. Nevertheless, sheep are the predominant animals of moorlands, having access to all three types of moorland community.

A major aim, therefore, is to manage moorland by a balanced mixture of grazing and burning, as the heather can be damaged and reduced in an area by overgrazing and by poor burning practice. The grazing pressure on the heather mostly depends on the proportion and nature of the grassland present, on the condition of the heather as maintained by periodic burns, and the interactions between them.

The major factors that can influence the choice of stocking density are as follows.

▶ As stocking rate is increased and the grassy areas become fully utilised, so the heather will be grazed both earlier in the season and more heavily.

▶ If the grassy areas are a small proportion of the total area, sheep numbers will be fewer than the tolerance of the heather to grazing would allow. This is because the diet quality from the small grass area needs to be maintained to achieve acceptable levels of animal performance. A density of sheep of less than one per two hectares is a guideline for pure heather moorland.

▶ If the grassy areas are a large proportion of the total area, their full exploitation carries an increasing risk that heather could be overgrazed;

Table 5.2 Examples of management programmes for lowland heath sites requiring basal or seed heather regeneration where grazing both is and is not possible

Basal heather regeneration stands when grazing is possible		Basal heather regeneration stands when grazing is not possible	
Year 1	Spray 'Asulam' in late July	Year 1	Spray 'Asulam' in late July
Year 1	Flail vegetation in winter	Year 1	Flail vegetation in winter
Year 3	Introduce summer grazing to control bracken and birch, and prevent build-up of heather wood	Each following year	Cut bracken once annually in mid-July as required and, if necessary, a birch control herbicide
		or	
		Year 1	Spray 'Asulam' in late July
		Year 1	Flail vegetation in winter
		Year 4	Re-spray 'Asulam' and, if necessary, a birch control herbicide

Heather seed regeneration stands when grazing is possible		Heather seed regeneration stands when grazing is not possible	
Years 1, 2 and 3	Stock a very high density of animals in spring before bracken emergence, to promote heather germination. Supply the feed which would normally be given by the farmer at this season	Year 1	Flail vegetation and rotovate the soil to stimulate heather seed germination
		Years 2, 3 and 4	Cut bracken twice annually, in mid-June and late July. This will prevent rapid expansion of grass and cowberry
Year 3	Flail the vegetation in winter	Year 5	Spray 'Asulam' in late July and, if necessary, a birch control herbicide
Year 4	Spray 'Asulam' in late July		
Each following year	Introduce mixed summer grazing to a level sustainable by the vegetation. This will damage bracken, check tree seedling growth and prevent build-up of heather wood		

(Source: Daniels, 1985)

to avoid overuse and damage, the number of sheep having access to the heather area has to be controlled. In this case an average density of one sheep per hectare is necessary, with preferably fewer on the areas of heather.

There are, however, no simple, generally applicable guidelines. More precise guidance on stocking density for a specific farm should be sought from an appropriate source of advice (see the *Helpful Organisations* booklet in the foundation module). However, poor burning management causes localised overgrazing and can result in the gradual elimination of heather *irrespective* of the number of sheep carried.

The primary aim of burning is to remove the ageing stands and restore the vegetation to a condition where the young growth is more accessible to grazing animals. Most heather should be burned when it reaches 20–30 centimetres high, although some should be left until it is 40 centimetres high. The frequency of burning of a particular area depends on how many years it takes the stand to reach maturity. The proportion of the total area requiring burning in any one year will reflect this time period (if it takes 12 years, then the aim should be to burn one-twelfth of the total each year, etc.). Management by burning should also aim to create a mosaic pattern of variously aged heather patches, to meet the needs of the grouse and to encourage the sheep to graze over a wide area. This demands that burned areas should be small (1 to 2 hectares), and preferably long and narrow (20 to 30 metres) wide.

It is important to distinguish widespread overgrazing from localised overgrazing. The former indicates that stock numbers are too high, the latter that either burning management or winter feeding practice needs reviewing. Too frequent burning of accessible areas, poor distribution and size of burned patches, and underburning all cause localised overgrazing, the heather being gradually replaced, usually by poor quality, grass-dominant vegetation. The cure lies in adopting good burning practice as a matter of urgency.

Winter feeding of supplements is another cause of localised overgrazing and the choice of feeding sites is important. Old heather recovers slowly from overgrazing and should be avoided; young heather can recover rapidly, providing it is rested for more than five years. If the feed is placed on heather, the most sensible strategy is to choose vigorous young heather for winter feeding sites, to move to a new area each year, even during the year if convenient, and to avoid returning to a previous site before the heather has recovered. If the feed is placed on grassy areas, less damage will be done to the heather (depending on its proximity), providing the feed is not placed in the same locality year after year. Where it is not practicable to use many feeding sites, or to change their location during the season, choose winter feeding areas that will be burning sites in the near future.

5.3   Deciding on options for managing your grassland, heath or moor

Having read in this chapter about the range of options that can be adopted to improve the conservation value of existing grassland, heath or moor, you should now decide which is most appropriate for the area you are studying. Remember to base the decision on your integrated assessment and on a careful consideration of the land manager's objectives. Section 5.4 gives some examples from the two case studies.

5.4   Options for managing the case study areas

Borders hill farm

Maintaining the cover and condition of the heather on the hill is important not only to the tenant farmer who reduces winter feeding costs but also to the owner who retains the game potential of the farm in the future. The establishment of a regular heather regeneration programme is required through both burning and an improved grazing regime.

Heather management

In previous years the problems of burning have been the lack of available labour coupled with the uncertainty over the weather conditions. This has resulted in insufficient fire control to ensure regular burning patterns. By swiping or cutting heather with a flail the farmer could:

1   define the boundaries of a burn and therefore aid the control of the size and direction of the burn, which could encourage smaller and more wide-spread burns;

2   stimulate heather regeneration when weather conditions are unfavourable for burning. A large amount of **brash** may result, especially from cutting the more mature areas of heather, suppressing regeneration. The brash must therefore be burned when conditions have improved or be removed and burned off-site. This method is possibly less favourable than burning because of the extra time needed to remove material and the reliance on vegetative propagation from heather stumps which decreases with age.

A neighbouring farmer has a flail which could be hired for a time during the burning season to allow initially the cutting of fire-break boundaries:

cost = £14.25 per hectare.

Under controlled conditions the regeneration of heather by burning stimulates regrowth. To maximise heather utilisation and its ability to regenerate, heather must be burned at the right stage, i.e. when it is 20 to 30 centimetres high. In this area heather may take 10 to 12 years to reach this height. Therefore, as a rough guide, approximately 10% of the hill should be burned every year:

10% of hill land = 80 hectares
80 hectares burned at £5.50 per hectare = £440.

In addition to burning, grazing by livestock can have similar effects on stimulating heather regrowth at sympathetic stocking densities. More effective dispersal of sheep over the hill and so the utilisation of heather may be improved by the use of feed blocks and 'fothering' (feeding) sites.

▶   Avoid placing feed blocks on areas of heather. If impractical, place feed blocks on vigorous 10- to 15-year-old heather which can recover more readily from localised grazing and trampling pressures.

▶   Feed blocks should be moved frequently (every two weeks, more than 20 metres from the previous site) and/or more blocks located on the heft. Fothering sites should be moved every three weeks, more than 250 metres from the existing site.

Greater control of the burn size and its siting will help reduce the incidence of the fire edge running into areas of bracken, helping to reduce its spread. Where the topography of the land allows, bracken could be controlled by mechanical cutting. Approximately 30 hectares are suitable for cutting on the areas of acidic grassland 30 hectares at £14.25 per hectare = £427.50.

An alternative is chemical control by the relatively specific 'Asulam' which requires two applications per year. On the less steep slopes application can be made by tractor sprayer: 30 hectares at £60 per hectare = £1800.

On the majority of the hill land chemicals will have to be applied by aerial spraying, after consultation with the relevant organisations, i.e. NCCS and the River Purification Board:

> approximately 20% of the hill area is affected – estimate
> treatment of 10% of area each year –
> 34 hectares per year at £135 per hectare = £4590.

Excluding stock grazing by fencing off plots on the hill will allow natural regeneration of the heather. To aid this regrowth, before enclosure, areas of heather could be cut and the brash spread to disperse the seeds and/or the soil could be scarified to encourage seed germination. Under the grant regulations, stock must be excluded for a period of five years although grazing after two years may be permitted.

On larger areas of the farm the removal of livestock over the autumn and winter from the hill or heft will reduce damage to the heather. This is a difficult option for the farmer because:

▶ grazing must be found either on the in-bye land or on a lowland farm over the winter

▶ if a tenant farmer, a reduction in rental should be given as an incentive.

The latter two options (i.e. stock exclusion and stock removal) are not applicable to the case study farm as a high grazing density is not the problem. Rather, it is the condition of the heather and therefore its utilisation by sheep which could be improved by burning and so lead to improved sheep movement over the hill.

Grant aid

The following grant aid could be sought from the Scottish Office Agriculture and Fisheries Department (SOAFD) Farm and Conservation Grant Scheme (EC and National):

▶ regeneration of heather by burning and cutting and control of bracken;

▶ enclosure of areas of grazed woodland, heather moorland and heathland.

The rate of grant is 50% of costs for farmers in less favoured areas.

Game

With the improvement in habitat and an increase in the control of pests in the area – fox control in March/April and carrion crow control in April/May – there may be potential to increase the commercial value of the grouse shooting. This would be in the form of a walk-up shoot only, as the re-establishment of grouse numbers to driven shoot standard would probably not be viable in terms of costs and the size of the remaining moorland area.

Walk-up shoots require 15 to 20 brace of grouse to be shot per day, let for £40 to 50 per brace to six to eight guns over the season. This would require five years of capital injection by the landowner before seeing a return.

Stelling Minnis Common

The new Managers of Stelling Minnis Common have, at the time of writing, still to decide on which of the possible options actually to implement. However, some preliminary work has been done on the possibilities arising from the community meeting, including some costings. The options for management considered so far centre on the need to maintain the open areas of the Common, without resorting to large-scale clearance of mature scrub.

1 Mowing

Essentially a holding or tidying operation, mowing is necessary when large areas are ungrazed or at a low stocking rate. It is not ecologically beneficial unless cuttings can be removed (e.g. a hay crop), but it is useful and without complications where large areas of free public access are involved. Mowing will not alone control bracken.

The Friends of Stelling Minnis currently raise money to pay for mowing, scrub clearance and other maintenance work done by the Conservators. Nix (1991) gives a farmer's cost for grass mowing (which should be comparable to this situation) of £12.75 per hectare.

For the Common 50 hectares x £12.75 = £637.50 for each cut but not all of it is mown, so, say, it costs £500 per cut. It is likely to be cut once a year, with no returns, except for the area cut for hay.

2 Grazing

Grazing is traditional, attractive and ecologically beneficial. However, it would need much more labour input and stock to bring it up to levels which can manage the Common without cutting as well, unless the livestock could be confined to specific areas. The present use is therefore symbolic rather than effective. By law a common may not be fenced, so other means are necessary for confining stock. An alternative for preventing stock wandering is using electronic collars (the collar triggers a cable that is buried around the perimeter of the area and gives the animal a small shock if it crosses). Roads could be fitted with cattle grids. These are both expensive items, and grids are not universally popular (noisy) and collars have not been proved very effective on sheep.

Fourteen commoners paid £70 each to buy ewes with lambs and they all have to pay vets' bills and £20 per year each for winter keep. The commoners would like to increase their flock to 200 ewes and employ a shepherd. Nix (1991) says that one full-time shepherd can look after 400 ewes and lambs, with help at lambing, shearing and dipping times. So a part- (half)time shepherd might be employed, at a salary of £4000 per year at a conservative estimate. Nix (1991) gives a gross margin (GM) for lowland sheep, at a low performance level, of £19.80 per ewe. So, approximately £20 x 200 sheep = GM £4000, i.e. the shepherd's salary is barely covered.

Other potential costs include:

Fencing   £1.20 per metre plus 60p labour
Troughs   £45–50 each
Cattle grids   £60,000 each at a 1991 estimate
Electronic collars £80 per animal at a 1991 estimate

With the present poor sheep prices, increasing the flock is hardly viable without some other subsidy. The present small flock tends not to stray, making grids and collars unnecessary. Could a larger flock be as docile, without careful breeding from the same stock to retain the sense of territory? Would additional problems of dog worrying and residents' complaints increase? What would be the optimum numbers of animals to satisfy these factors and apply grazing to maintain the Common satisfactorily?

3   Scrub and bracken control/clearance

Control could be done by hand at early stages. Clearance is contentious, and may be ecologically damaging. Cut stumps could be herbicide-treated – which is also contentious. Scrub is of great value to birds, but loses its value when it is too dense (and the ground flora disappears). Rotational clearance of small patches is an option to preserve the mosaic landscape.

Bracken is very destructive and has few friends, but no 'soft' approaches are effective. Present management tends to encourage not discourage bracken. Hand cutting or herbicide treatment of selected areas (temporarily fenced) are options.

Scrub clearance and bracken cutting come under costs borne by the Conservators (see point 1 above). Some relevant costs include the following.

▶   *Scrub* – using herbicide, e.g. 'Triclopyr', to treat stumps: Nix (1991) gives a cost of £58 per hectare for this use in forestry. Pulling out scrub with a tractor and chain may be more desirable and cost-effective, or retaining scrub and cutting in blocks on a rotation (bush cutting = £7.15 per hour).

▶   Bracken – using herbicide, e.g. 'Asulox', to treat areas; Nix (1991) gives a cost of £70–80 per hectare for applying herbicide around young trees in forestry. The Countryside Stewardship Scheme (CSS) pays £85 per hectare for bracken clearance on lowland heath. This needs careful follow-up treatment, e.g. heather re-establishment.

4   Formal access (car parking)

Car access to Stelling Minnis Common may be regarded as a necessary evil, although some people feel that it is excessive. The options range from total restriction to charging for parking. Car access to the Common could be limited to certain areas, perhaps with better all-weather surfacing. Scrub could be cut back along the Bossington road where it restricts visibility.

Should an all-weather, formal car-parking surface be proposed for limited areas? Recent local contractor's prices are:

Timber edging board	£1.50 per metre
To strip 200 mm topsoil plus mound on site	£2.50 per cubic metre
To replace with 200 mm roadstone sub-base over 'Terram' layer	£5.10 per cubic metre
Any grading of site	15p per square metre.

These are very low prices, but, say, it will cost under £10 per square metre plus the cost of the edging board, and any fencing to restrict access further. Ministerial approval would be needed.

5   Pond restoration

The few ponds on the Common (e.g. Coxsole Pond) tend to be overgrown with aquatic plants such as reedmace and/or surrounded by dense fringes of hawthorn and shrubby willows. Although non-intervention (natural succession) is an option, clearance would maintain them as natural features, which are unusual on the Downs. Not so easy, however, would be to line them. Recent dry summers may have cracked linings or made them vulnerable to disturbance.

Pond restoration could be done by hand, using Conservation Volunteers or local volunteers.

Costs: a Hymac-type excavator at £16 per hour plus transport cost, average £50. This might clear all the ponds in one to two days.

6 Regeneration of heather

Loss of heathland vegetation, especially the heather itself, is causing concern. An adjunct to a more extensive grazing programme might be some attempt to re-establish areas of heather, through measures such as bracken clearance, light cultivation, spreading heather cuttings that bear ripe seed and follow-up grazing. Sufficient parent material would be needed either on site or from a local seed source; in which case it is probably realistic only on a small scale.

Harvested heather shoots which bear mature seed capsules, or commercial supplies of heather seed capsules, could be used. Detailed advice would be needed from e.g. the Nature Conservancy Council. Harvesting could be done with a forage harvester or a flail mower and baler to take from good existing areas, e.g. fire-breaks. It is doubtful whether Stelling Minnis Common could supply enough material for this scale so the nearest next source (Hothfield) needs investigating. Literature suggests that heather seeds would cost as little as £150 per hectare (1988) – probably more if transport from a distant site is needed.

7 Labour

Contract labour is needed – for one-off specialist operations, e.g. pond contractor, herbicide control of scrub/bracken.

Retained labour is needed for continuous input, e.g. mowing (as done now), shepherding.

Conservation Volunteers are needed for light hand work, e.g. coppicing, pond clearance.

Much of the work on Stelling Minnis Common should be tackled quite easily with a strong local community interested in its own backyard; there will be more sense of the Common belonging to people if they look after it themselves. Contractors should be used only as a last resort.

8 Materials in kind

Kent County Council might provide 'sheep grazing' signs, or contribute to the cost of cattle grids.

Local firms might sponsor e.g. pond clearance or hand tools.

9 Grants

Kent County Council provides Countryside Conservation Grants – e.g. for pond restoration, pollarding – of about 50%.

The Nature Conservancy Council provides Small Grants – e.g. for fencing – of 50%. Both need prior approval.

Under the Countryside Stewardship Scheme (CSS) the Common would be categorised as lowland heathland and would need an application (discretionary) to join. A 10-year management plan should include light summer grazing, cutting/mowing, bracken control and scrub management. The CSS pays £50 per hectare per year for managing existing heath, plus a supplement for access of £50 per hectare per year, plus a supplement for the regeneration of lowland heath of £50 per hectare per year over five years as part of a management plan.

Chapter 6

RE-CREATING GRASSLANDS, HEATHS AND MOORS

This chapter deals with the creation of new grassland, heath or moor on areas which have been extensively disturbed or affected by intensive agricultural production, building or mineral workings, and where conservation is an important priority for the land manager. In many cases the aim is to re-create gradually or restore a particular habitat type that used to be found on the land concerned, but sometimes it can mean rapidly developing a 'green-field' site to provide a conservation area of a more general nature. In both cases, once established, the management of the vegetation will be the same as described in Chapter 5. In general, it is reasonable to consider the re-creation of lowland grassland habitats and the restoration of lowland and upland heathland separately, even though some of the techniques are similar.

6.1 Re-creating grassland habitats

There are many factors to be considered in trying to re-create a flower-rich grassland. They include the soil type, the current vegetation, the source and mix of new seed, and the actual method of establishment. Remember, too, that most semi-natural grasslands have taken decades, and often centuries, to reach their high levels of plant species diversity. Although plant species diversity can be developed quite quickly in new grasslands, it still takes many years for the sward to develop fully. Indeed, the nature of vegetation dynamics means that the sward is ever-changing, if imperceptibly. Furthermore, a high plant species diversity does not automatically produce a high animal species diversity, as colonisation of a site, particularly by invertebrates, depends on the proximity of similar habitats and the mobility of species. Nevertheless, the introduction of animal species, such as a butterfly, to a new grassland should be considered only in exceptional circumstances, as it would normally involve removal from another habitat site and may also require a special licence under the Wildlife and Countryside Act (see the *Legislation and Regulations* booklet in the foundation module). If the possibility of introducing an animal species is being considered expert advice should be sought from the Nature Conservancy Council or the County Wildlife Trust before proceeding.

Site selection

The integrated assessment of an area should have identified possible sites for the re-creation of a grassland habitat. Examples include long-disturbed areas such as arable land and mineral workings; recently disturbed transport and other building sites; or existing grass swards of very poor wildlife value, such as single-species grass leys and intensively improved permanent pasture for grazing animals; or amenity grassland that is mown frequently. In some cases the site will be chosen because it has a particular soil type, drainage pattern or topography. All of these features will influence the method of establishment, as will the state of the current vegetation, in particular the presence of perennial weeds such as thistles, nettles, dock and couch grass.

Seed selection

For sowing new grassland it is preferable to use native seed and if possible seed of local **provenance**. Using native seed maintains the ecological integrity of British habitats, avoids the possible introduction of non-native species in the seed mixture, and ensures that the plants will be of genetic stock that is well adapted to the soils and prevailing climate. The majority of seed for sale is native but it is always worth asking the supplier about its origin and also how it has been produced (whether harvested from semi-natural grassland or from specially grown plots).

One way of ensuring that the seed is native and of local provenance is to allow natural regeneration from the seed-bank and colonisation from nearby existing sites. Although floristic diversity can develop quite rapidly in disturbed ground, it can happen only when suitable seed sources are present. Short-term disturbance of a site will not significantly reduce the seed-bank, whereas areas under arable cultivation for many years will have fewer desirable species left.

The increasing rarity of semi-natural grassland habitats, particularly in predominantly arable areas, and the poor seed dispersal mechanisms of many plants, mean that in many areas there are few natural sources of seed, and natural colonisation is less likely to produce a typical species-rich grassland habitat, making the production of 'artificial' grasslands a necessity (see Box 6.1).

Natural colonisation may be slow but it can be speeded up by colonisation from existing sources through collecting seed or spreading hay bales. Collecting seed of certain 'protected species' is prohibited by the Wildlife and Countryside Act 1981, and so should be avoided (see the *Legislation and Regulations* booklet in the foundation module for details). Collecting enough seed by hand is also time-consuming. The spreading of hay bales from flower-rich meadows, and hence the seeds that they contain, can sometimes be effective in enriching existing swards; but it may be less satisfactory on a disturbed site as it does not always ensure an even sward cover (but see below). Bare patches then provide sites for erosion or establishment points for undesirable perennial weed species.

Seed mixtures are divided into four main types: those suitable for clay soils, chalk and limestone soils, alluvial soils and dry acid soils. Within these limits the selection of species for inclusion in a seed mixture is determined by personal choice, by the land manager's objectives, the characteristics of the site, the mixtures or range of seeds available, and the costs involved.

Where the aim is *to re-create an existing type of semi-natural grassland*, the choice of species is determined by the composition of the plant community within that grassland. Nevertheless, all habitat types show considerable local and regional variation and so a limited basic range of widespread species would be preferable to start with, rather than using a very complex mixture. Natural colonisation or artificial enhancement can then supplement these basic species. Moreover, the composition of the sward, once established, will

Box 6.1   A tale of two grasslands

Until recently, there has been little research in Great Britain on how easily – and how quickly – wildflowers, sedges and grasses will recolonise abandoned arable fields, simply because arable land has rarely been abandoned since the 1930s – and hence during the development of modern ecology.

A study published in 1987 of a 10-hectare Oxfordshire field, last cultivated for cereals in 1981, found that no less than 212 species of flowers and grasses had established themselves after just five years. And there was more! The rose-coloured, long-stalked cranesbill – a flower that had not been seen anywhere in that part of Oxfordshire for at least 30 years – made a comeback, along with many breeding insects, including brown argus and marbled white butterflies.

No less than 43 of the 75 limestone grassland flowering plants – such as the yellow common rock-rose, the white fairy flax and the pink restharrow – which grew on permanent limestone grasslands nearby (those which had probably never been under the plough) had reappeared within five years, although their abundance was not measured.

In contrast, another study published in 1988 of some grassland overlying chalk in Sussex, which has been developing since 1976 when wheat-growing ceased, found that few chalk grassland plants re-established themselves. What is worse, the study area is in a Sussex valley that is completely surrounded by rich chalk grassland, a seemingly potent source of seed.

Seed dispersal from the chalk grassland was found to reach only as far as the areas of old arable land immediately adjacent. When the seed-bank (seeds and fruits on or beneath the soil surface that can germinate) was examined on the former arable land, only seeds of weed species were found – such as the scarlet pimpernel and creeping buttercup – these being associated with frequent soil disturbance and cultivation, but few other species.

Of the seedlings that emerged, no more than 10 of the species represented per square metre were typical of chalk grassland and even these were minor constituents. Rich chalk grassland has 20 or 30 species in every square metre of vegetation by comparison. And only 15% of all the germinating seedlings were species that are normally found in this type of grassland, whether they came from the seed-bank or from seed raining down onto the soil from the surrounding grassland plants.

change within a few years due to ecological and management factors. Thus some original species may quickly disappear, while new species will arise from the seed-bank or from nearby sources. Even the persistent species can fluctuate greatly in number from year to year.

If the aim is simply *to create an attractive flower-rich grassland*, simple mixtures of common, widely distributed species can be sown to produce 'new' communities with no natural counterpart. In most cases available mixtures are designed for use on specific soil types or selected planting schemes. These may range from quick cover requirements after the completion of a road construction project, covering derelict land, reclaiming very poor industrial sites for future leisure uses, creating meadow-type grasslands, woodland or hedgerow replanting, or upgrading the wildflower content of farm tracks, **headlands** and 'set-aside' areas.

Some general criteria have proved useful in selecting plant species for inclusion in wildflower seed mixtures. Species should be:

▶   ecologically suitable for particular soil/water conditions;

▶   common grassland species;

> not rare or locally distributed;

> preferably perennial and long-lived;

> colourful with attractive flowers;

> attractive to insects as nectar or pollen sources;

> not highly competitive or invasive;

> those with seed which germinates easily over a range of temperature conditions and preferably without dormancy mechanisms.

A list of species meeting many of these requirements is given in Table 6.1.

Wildflower mixtures are normally sown mixed with grasses. The relative proportions by weight are usually 80% grasses and 20% wildflowers (sometimes 85% grasses and 15% wildflowers). Sometimes it may be preferable to begin with a perennial grass mixture only, examples of which are shown in Table 6.2. There are both ecological and economic reasons why grasses should form the major component in any sward. First, grasses account for about 60% of the above-ground cover in the majority of semi-natural grassland, more so in the winter months. Secondly, if properly selected, grasses can withstand mowing, grazing and trampling. Thirdly, herbaceous plants die down in winter and without grasses would leave bare or untidy patches. Lastly, grass seed is relatively cheap and available in large quantities commercially; while in contrast many herbaceous species are harder to multiply, are not available in large quantities and thus are much more expensive. Examples of typical grass/ wildflower mixtures are shown in Table 6.3.

It is important to know the genetic origin of the grass species chosen as there are several cultivars available for some species. Agricultural cultivars of perennial rye-grass, cocksfoot, tall fescue and timothy grasses are totally unsuitable for conservation purposes because of their vigour and productivity. There are also many so-called 'low-maintenance' cultivars for use in amenity grasslands which may be suitable but have not been fully tested, and so should be avoided if possible at present.

As was mentioned in Chapter 5, attractive grasslands can be established within two to four years using seed collected from species-rich meadows. Methods for harvesting, cleaning and storing seed have been developed, but obtaining a pure sample and useful seed yields is difficult. This is because flowers and hence seed are produced over a period of time, different species flowering at different times. There are also large year-to-year fluctuations in seed production in individual species, while the height and shape of species vary widely. Thus the harvesting process itself can miss collecting seed of many species that are present in the community; harvesting too early may result in a high proportion of unripe seeds, whereas harvesting late will result in much seed being shed and lost. All these factors make the seed very expensive to collect, although on the plus side hay bales can contain the seeds of many grassland species which are unobtainable from commercial sources.

Seed from hay

One way of reducing costs is to harvest the seed-rich hay either as bales or as loose hay and then to spread it on the land without separating out the seeds. Successful establishment depends on the hay layer not being too thick, to prevent germination of desirable species, and on subsequent weather conditions (wet conditions encouraging rotting of seeds). Alternatively, the hay can be chopped up to reduce its smothering effect when spread on the soil.

Table 6.1 The suitability of plant species for different soil types

	Clay	Chalk and limestone	Alluvial	Dry acid
Grasses				
Common bent	●		●	●
Silver hair-grass				●
Meadow foxtail	●		●	
Sweet vernal	●		●	●
Meadow brome	●		●	
Upright brome		○		
Crested dogstail	●	●	●	
Wavy hair-grass				●
Sheep's fescue		●		●
Chewings fescue	●	●	●	●
Red fescue	●	●	●	●
Fine-leaved sheep's fescue				●
Meadow barley	●		●	
Timothy	●	●	●	
Smooth meadow-grass	●		●	
Rough-stalked meadow-grass	●		●	
Golden oat grass	●	●	●	
Herbs				
Yarrow	●	●	●	
Kidney vetch		●		
Lesser knapweed	○	○		
Greater knapweed		○		
Wild basil		●		
Pignut			●	
Smooth hawksbeard				●
Wild carrot	●	●	●	
Common storksbill				●
Meadowsweet	●	●		
Heath bedstraw				●
Lady's bedstraw	●	●	●	
Dovesfoot cranesbill				●
Meadow cranesbill	○			
Mouse-ear hawkweed		●		
Horseshoe vetch		●		
Common catsear	●		●	●
Field scabious	○	○		
Rough hawkbit	●	●		

(continued)

Table 6.1 (continued)

	Clay	Chalk and limstone	Alluvial	Dry acid
Ox-eye daisy	●	●	●	
Birdsfoot trefoil	○	○	○	
Ragged robin	●		●	
Musk mallow	●			
Black medick	●	●		
Sainfoin		○		
Restharrow	●	●		
Spiny restharrow	●	●		
Burnet saxifrage		●		
Ribwort plantain	●	●	●	
Hoary plantain	●	●		
Tormentil				●
Cowslip	●	●	●	
Self-heal	●	●	●	
Meadow buttercup	●		●	
Bulbous buttercup	●	●		
Yellow rattle	●	●	●	
Sorrel	●		●	●
Sheep's sorrel				●
Salad burnet	●	●		
Great burnet			●	
Meadow saxifrage	●			
Pepper saxifrage	●		●	
White campion	●	●	●	
Betony	●			
Lesser stitchwort			●	
Haresfoot clover				●
Hop trefoil	●	●		
Lesser trefoil	●	●		
Tufted vetch	●		●	
Common vetch	○	○	○	
Smooth tare	●	●	●	

Soil type

(Source: Wells *et al.*, 1989)

● Suitable

o May be too vigorous on fertile soil

Table 6.2   Examples of perennial grass mixtures (figures are percentage by weight)

1 General purpose mixture			3 Mixture for moist loamy soils		
	Sheep's fescue	50		Red fescue	40
	Red fescue	40		Meadow barley	20
	Smooth meadow-grass	10		Golden oat grass	20
2 Mixture for calcareous soils				Meadow foxtail	20
	Sheep's fescue	50	4 Mixture for acid soils		
	Red fescue	20		Common bent	40
	Smaller catstail	10		Wavy hair-grass	30
	Smooth meadow-grass	10		Fine-leaved sheep's fescue	20
	Golden oat grass	10		Sweet vernal	10
	also quaking grass –				
	using pot-grown plants				

Table 6.3   Examples of typical grass/wildflower mixtures (figures are percentage by weight)

1 Mixture for use on calcareous soil		2 Mixture for use on clay soils	
Wildflowers		**Wildflowers**	
Agrimony	2.0	Betony	2.0
Birdsfoot trefoil	1.0	Birdsfoot trefoil	1.0
Clustered bellflower	1.0	Bulbous buttercup	0.5
Cowslip	1.0	Cowslip	1.0
Field scabious	0.5	Field scabious	1.0
Goatsbeard	1.0	Goatsbeard	0.5
Greater knapweed	0.5	Hoary plantain	1.0
Harebell	0.5	Lady's bedstraw	1.0
Hoary plantain	1.0	Lesser knapweed	0.5
Lady's bedstraw	1.0	Meadow buttercup	1.5
Lesser knapweed	0.5	Meadow cranesbill	0.5
Meadowsweet	1.0	Meadow saxifrage	0.5
Ox-eye daisy	1.0	Meadowsweet	1.0
Ribwort plantain	1.0	Musk mallow	0.5
Rough hawkbit	0.5	Ox-eye daisy	1.0
Salad burnet	2.0	Ribwort plantain	1.0
Self-heal	1.5	Salad burnet	1.0
Small scabious	0.5	Self-heal	2.0
Sorrel	0.5	Sorrel	0.5
Wild carrot	1.0	White campion	1.0
Wild marjoram	0.25	Wild carrot	0.5
Yellow rattle	<u>0.5</u>	Yarrow	<u>0.5</u>
	20.0		20.0
Grasses		**Grasses**	
Chewings fescue	25.0	Chewings fescue	4.0
Crested dogstail	9.0	Crested dogstail	25.0
Quaking grass	1.0	Dwarf creeping fescue	20.0
Red fescue	25.0	Meadow foxtail	10.0
Sheep's fescue	<u>20.0</u>	Quaking grass	1.0
	80.0	Rough-stalked meadow-grass	<u>20.0</u>
			80.0

(Source: Anon., 1990b)

In both cases there are problems of obtaining continuous plant cover and not allowing arable weeds that are already present in the soil to flourish in patches of bare ground.

Establishing flower-rich grasslands on disturbed ground

The key to establishing a good grassland/wildflower sward is to ensure careful selection of the seed mixture, to produce a weed-free and well-prepared seed-bed and to manage the site carefully, especially in the first year.

Site preparation

One step in site preparation that should not be omitted is the removal of all perennial weeds such as thistle, nettle, dock and couch grass. A little effort at this stage will yield long-term dividends. Perennial weeds can be success-fully controlled with a systemic herbicide. In heavy infestations the herbi-cide may be used as a foliar spray. In lighter infestations individual weeds can be spot-treated with a dilute solution using a knapsack sprayer. The chemical manufacturer's recommendations and safety instructions must be strictly followed whichever method of application is used. If weeds are removed by digging, care should be taken to remove whole roots and not to allow fragments to remain for regeneration in the future. Any drainage that may be necessary should occur at this stage. Excessive hedgerow growth, brambles, scrap iron or building rubble should also be removed.

Soil preparation

Most wildflowers can survive on a soil of low fertility where competition from aggressive species is reduced. Never add fertiliser to the site except when sowing taller grasses on infertile sub-soils, where a very light application may assist establishment. If the richer top soil can be removed then the underlying soil will produce a better herb-rich sward. On sites with extremely poor soils such as exposed sub-soil, quarry workings, and crushed bricks from redevelopment sites, it may also be necessary to spread a thin layer of top soil for initial plant establishment. However, most sites will have more normal soil conditions. Where possible the soil should be cultivated so as to be extra fine but it should have a good tilth and be free of stones to allow good seed covering after sowing.

A common fault with seed-beds is that they are too loose and uneven. The seed-bed should be both fine and firm, which is usually achieved by repeated harrowing and rolling, the timing of these operations in respect of the weather being crucial to success. Disturbing the soil too much to obtain a good tilth may result in too much soil moisture being lost, inhibiting germination of some species. The periods most suitable both for soil preparation and for sowing are usually the spring and autumn. Other periods may be used for sowing but under conditions of drought, or cold, seed will not germinate until more favourable conditions prevail. Seed should not be sown onto land which is likely to be exposed to flooding, or significant water run-off, until a relatively dry period is expected.

Methods of soil preparation will vary with the site and the scale of the project. Hand digging or rotovating may be sufficient for a small-scale project. Ploughing, harrowing, discing or rotovating will be necessary for large-scale projects. If a heavy annual weed seed population is likely in the soil the site can be left fallow for a short period to encourage its growth. Once germinated these weeds can then be killed by spraying or cultivating before sowing the seed mixtures. Light infestations of annual weeds can be left to act as a nurse crop for the wildflower seedlings as they will present no long-term problems.

On most sites, especially amenity areas such as roadside verges or country parks, it is essential that a vegetation cover is established quickly, both to prevent soil erosion and for aesthetic reasons. To meet this requirement, it is often beneficial to sow a quick-growing annual nurse crop which will germinate quickly and then die back, allowing the wildflowers and other grasses to replace it. Other advantages of a nurse crop are that it tends to suppress excessive annual weed growth and provides shelter for the slower growing wildflowers.

Nurse crop

Westerwold's rye-grass has all these characteristics and is widely used, although it can be too vigorous on more fertile soils. It is sown with the chosen seed mixture at about 3 to 4.5 grams per square metre. Using Westerwold's will ensure an 80% ground cover within 10 weeks of sowing. Westerwold's is an annual and, providing it is cut before it sheds its seeds, it will disappear from the sward within two years.

Seeds of the various species within the wildflower mixture vary considerably in size, shape and texture and therefore need careful handling. The wildflowers and grasses should be mixed thoroughly both before and during sowing to ensure a uniform distribution across the site. As the quantities of seed being sown are often small a greater degree of uniformity can be achieved by mixing the seed with an inert substance such as sawdust, barley meal or dry sand in the ratio of 1:3. On larger sites uniformity of sowing can also be achieved by dividing the site into several sectors of equal size and sowing with weighed quantities of seed, rather than sowing the whole area with all the seed at once.

Seed sowing

On small areas the most efficient method of seed sowing is broadcast sowing by hand. On larger areas seed may be applied using tractor-mounted machinery such as fertiliser spreaders, cereal seed drills, and slot seeders. Equipment for seed sowing can be hired from local agricultural machinery merchants or provided by contractors.

Once sown the seed should be covered by light raking or harrowing and rolling with a flat roller. On larger sites light harrowing and rolling with a ring-type roller should be sufficient. Both methods ensure good contact between seed and soil and encourage rapid germination and establishment.

Steep slopes, and other difficult terrain, such as exposed rock and sub-soil in transport construction projects, reclaimed quarry or industrial workings, may require another method for seed placement. Seeds can be sprayed onto such sites using the **hydroseeding** method. For particularly harsh terrain, mulches and nutrients can be incorporated into the spray applications to help trap the seeds in place. This method of seeding is best done by specialised contractors.

Typical sowing rates for different seed mixtures are:

Sowing rates

▶ wildflowers and grasses $3-4 \text{ g/m}^2$ (30–40 kg/ha);
▶ perennial wildflowers only 1 g/m^2 (10 kg/ha);
▶ annual wildflowers mixture 2 g/m^2 (20 kg/ha);
▶ grass seeds only $2-4 \text{ g/m}^2$ (20–40 kg/ha).

The lower seeding rates for wildflower seed mixtures are designed to allow the successful establishment of the slower growing wildflowers. The higher seeding rates are required for grass mixtures in order to produce an adequate sward.

Good site preparation and seed sowing in themselves are not the sole requirements for good habitat creation. However, if these are the only activities possible, such as after motorway or road construction, an attractive habitat of low maintenance cost can be obtained. Obviously it will not be as botanically diverse as a more intensively managed site.

In most other situations, management during the first year after sowing is crucial both to the establishment and to the final composition of the grassland community. The priority in the first few months is to control competition from annual weeds and perennial weeds such as broad-leaved dock.

Newly sown sites may well show a flush of annual weed seedlings, such as common chickweed, nettle and scentless mayweed. If this flush is very dense it may be necessary to kill it off using a selective broad-leaved herbicide. Any grass seedlings will not be damaged and the slower growing wildflowers would not have emerged at this early stage. If the annual weed seedling population is low it may be left to act as a nurse crop to protect the slower growing wildflowers. In the second and subsequent years the wildflowers will prevent any further growth of annual weeds. If docks or other perennial weeds appear to be a potential nuisance, spot-treatment with a systemic herbicide, applied by a rope-wick applicator or a knapsack sprayer is effective.

As weeds tend to germinate quickly and have high growth rates, they can be controlled by cutting. Plots sown in spring and mid-summer should be cut to a height of about 8–10 centimetres, six to eight weeks after sowing, and well before any seeds have set. The precise time to cut should be judged by how much the weeds or the nurse crop have grown. Cutting at this time will effectively reduce competition from weeds and in many cases kill the taller species completely. The cuttings should be removed if possible. No such cutting should occur, however, where annual wildflowers have been added to the mixture to give first year colour.

At this stage, the developing grassland is structurally three-layered: (i) the nurse crop (if sown) or weeds, 10–20 centimetres tall; (ii) sown grasses, 4–8 centimetres tall; and (iii) broad-leaved plants, mostly in the cotyledon or first true leaf stage, less than 2 centimetres tall. The aim of cutting is to allow the herbs in the lowest layer to develop alongside the sown grasses, without too much competition from weeds or the nurse crop. The number of cuts depends on soil fertility and growing conditions. On infertile sites, only two cuts may be needed in the first year; on a highly fertile site, five or more cuts may be necessary. The last cut will probably be made in late October, after careful observation of the sward and the relative heights of the various components.

In the second and subsequent years, the management requirements will be less, and the site can be treated as an established grassland habitat, being cut only once or twice. Spring and autumn cutting are recommended with a low (5 centimetres) cut in spring, followed by a second cut in the autumn after seeds have set. This usually means a cut in March to May, and another in September to October, depending on location and weather, although the precise timing depends on the stage of growth of the plant species. Clippings or trimmings should preferably be removed from the site. Long trimmings left in place cause the decay of vegetation underneath; small trimmings encourage the re-establishment of weeds such as creeping thistle. If the trimmings prove to be too costly to remove from the site a burning patch should be selected and used each year. Care should be taken to ensure the safety of personnel and surrounding vegetation when burning. Where burning is not possible, or is undesirable, a stacking system can be used. Trimmings should be collected and stacked in an area reserved for the purpose. Decomposition will follow but may take some time. If necessary the process of decomposition can be aided by adding small amounts of fertiliser to the stack. As with burning, stacking should occur at the same location each year to reduce any adverse effects on the site as a whole. Hay can also be harvested from meadow-type habitats in the conventional way.

Subsequent years

On larger sites, management costs can be reduced and a more attractive appearance can be achieved by rotational cutting, a different area being cut each year. This provides a succession of flowers and nectar sources at different times of the year, leaves refuges for animals, and allows the successful breeding of many insects. For example, cutting in mid-June when many plant species are already in full bloom will actually enable late-flowering species such as lady's bedstraw and burnet saxifrage to produce a splash of colour from late August through to October, when colour is scarce. Close-cutting of grassland in late autumn often provides the best conditions for early-flowering rosette species such as cowslip.

The females of several butterflies including the meadow brown, small heath and wall brown lay their eggs on taller grass stems. Since their eggs are laid at various times throughout the summer, they are very vulnerable to cutting (and heavy grazing) right up to the autumn, and so benefit from protected areas. To prevent colonisation of these refuges by unwanted scrub the uncut areas should be rotated from year to year.

In busy amenity areas a 'path' can be cut through the grass at regular intervals. Adjacent areas need not be cut as frequently. Areas still further away from the path need be cut only occasionally. This results in a more diverse sward and may help to reduce widespread trampling by the visiting public. Management costs are also reduced.

103

In towns and urban areas in general, it is often beneficial to keep the edges of wildflower areas closely mown and looking 'tidy', to draw attention to the wildflower mixture and to indicate that they are being managed and not just left. Attractive and carefully positioned notices to inform people that wildflower mixtures have been sown will often help to make such areas more acceptable and attractive to a public which has been conditioned to expect only short, mown, green grassland in urban areas.

There have been few attempts to manage areas sown with wildflower mixtures by grazing. This is because few wildflower mixtures have so far been sown on farmland and also because most sown areas are too small to support grazing animals for any length of time. There is no logical reason why livestock should not be used, and, as wildflower mixtures gain favour on farmland, sheep will increasingly be used for grazing them. Stock numbers may have to be kept low initially, during the establishment phase, but, as the sward increases in cover, sheep densities and time of year of grazing can be used to manipulate sward composition as on established pasture.

Establishing wildflowers in existing grass swards

Broadcasting

Broadcasting by hand or fertiliser spreader as a way of sowing wildflower seeds into an established sward without any pre-treatment is rarely successful. Dead plant material at the base of the sward prevents the seed from reaching the soil and, even if the seed germinates, competition from the established sward is intense and usually kills the seedling. Attempts at providing gaps in the sward by harrowing and at reducing competition by close mowing and re-mowing all trimmings before sowing the seed, followed by a light rolling, have been tried but have not been very successful. More research work is required on this and on the alternative of spreading seed-rich hay-bales over closely mown swards before any firm recommendations can be given.

Slot-seeding

If the area to be enriched with wildflowers already contains the desired species of grass, slot-seeding provides a way of achieving diversity without having to destroy the original sward. This involves spraying herbicide onto a band of the existing sward to kill it and then drilling the required species mixture into a slot cut into the ground within the sprayed band. It is believed that, in the absence of competition, the seed will germinate and the seedlings will grow to a competitive size before the grass sward recovers and spreads to fill the sprayed area (see also Box 6.2).

A slightly different procedure, called 'strip-seeding', involves rotovating 75 millimetre-wide strips, 225 millimetres apart. No herbicide is used and seed sown in the cultivated strip germinates in a relatively competition-free zone, competition from surrounding grasses being controlled by regular mowing. Strip-seeders were originally developed for introducing clover into grass swards and are now being used for introducing wildflower seeds into permanent grass with, it is claimed, some success.

Pot-grown plants

Wildflowers can be raised from seed in pots quite easily using conventional horticultural methods. Four- to five-month-old plants with about four true leaves are ideally sized for inserting into grassland using a bulb-planter. It is preferable to plant them in groups or drifts to enable easy cross-fertilisation. In specialist planting schemes, this technique is preferable to sowing straightforward grass/wildflower mixtures because it allows plants to be selected for particular habitat conditions and provides instant colour where quick results are required. It may also be more cost-effective for: (i) species

In a series of trials on heavy clay soils, a precision drill, with drills 50 centimetres apart, was used to introduce herbs into a three year-old ley, into permanent pastures and into a variety of amenity grasslands. Each drill was band sprayed (about 10 centimetres wide) with 'Paraquat'.

The most important points to emerge from these and other trials were as follows.

1 Twenty herb species, which varied considerably in seed size and shape, were established in a variety of swards.

2 Establishment between species varied considerably, but there were no total failures. Species which established particularly well were black knapweed, field scabious, meadow buttercup, cowslip and self-heal.

3 Better establishment was achieved with autumn rather than spring slot-seedings, probably because reinvasion of the sprayed band by grasses is much slower in the autumn and winter than in the spring.

4 A young sward without any accumulation of dead material provided better conditions for establishment than an old one with a thick layer of dead or moribund plant material. It may be advantageous to harrow old permanent grassland before slot-seeding to break up the layer of litter.

5 Regrowth of grasses after band spraying varied considerably between different cultivars.

6 Yellow rattle and birdsfoot trefoil sown in the autumn flowered the following year, but other species required another year's growth before they reached flowering size. The yellow rattle invaded the unsprayed grassland in the second year, but it is too early to say whether other species will behave in the same way.

(Source: from Wells *et al.*, 1986)

which are slow-growing and likely to be swamped by faster-growing species, e.g. harebell or large thyme; and (ii) species whose seed is expensive and/or difficult to germinate, e.g. oxlip, dropwort and meadow cranesbill. Using pot-grown plants is particularly suitable for enhancing existing grassland on small sites such as wildflower gardens and nature study areas in schools.

Observations made on plants inserted into roadside banks have confirmed that plants will flower in the year after planting and that survival rates are very good for a wide range of species.

6.2   Re-establishing heathland habitats

The re-establishment of both lowland heath and upland heather moorland habitats depends on the site conditions. Thus any conservation management can be divided into two categories.

▶   The *rehabilitation* or *restoration* of abandoned fields, which were recently created from heath, cleared forests, or areas where the heathland plant community has been seriously reduced by management practices, but where there may still be scattered heather plants and seeds in the seed bank to enable heather regeneration.

▶   The *re-creation* of heath on derelict areas, disused mineral workings, land damaged by construction work, long-improved grasslands and arable fields where establishment relies on the introduction of heather seeds or plants.

Rehabilitating severely damaged heathland areas

In severely damaged areas the main aim is to restore heathland vegetation by exposing the seed bank which remains in the soil or peat. This can be done using techniques such as mowing, rotovating, turf stripping or grazing. In each case the seeds are exposed and encouraged to germinate whilst trying to reduce the competition from other plants.

Turf stripping	Turf stripping has the advantage that nutrients are also removed with the upper layer of soil, helping to maintain a low nutrient status to offset any input from agriculture or pollution. (Nevertheless a single, light application of nitrogen after turf stripping enhances heather growth, but at the risk of altering the composition of the vegetation.) A major problem on heather moorland is that exposed peat requires protection from instability caused by sheep trampling, the cultivation method, and wind and rain. Erosion can be reduced by sowing companion grasses, such as wavy hair-grass, at low densities, or covering the area with forestry brashings.
Grazing	Light sheep grazing checks seedlings of invading woody species, but at higher densities the dung encourages grasses. However, sheep grazing alone on abandoned fields reclaimed from heath can also restore the heathland vegetation by suppressing the grass growth.
Burns	On heather moorland where the heather has become very old and largely replaced by purple moor-grass, regeneration can be facilitated by burning. More heather seedlings result if an area of old heath is burned twice in consecutive years rather than burned once, leaving charred stems. Also, seedling numbers are higher where sheep are prevented from grazing the newly burned areas.
	As with all restoration programmes it is preferable to work only on part of a site each year in order to create a mosaic of vegetation of different ages and possibly species composition. New areas will be very poor in insect species until the heather has aged and they will only increase if there are existing heaths in close proximity.

Re-creating heathland on disturbed ground

Re-seeding	Where there is little or no seed-bank in the soil, applying heather seeds or scattering litter or top soil containing seeds onto prepared areas may be needed. Seeds can be obtained from seed merchants but they are often expensive and not of native origin. Seeds may be collected from existing heath by hand or with a forage harvester. Either these seeds can be broadcast or heather plants can be raised from seeds or from cuttings and trans-planted. Protection from disturbance is essential and should continue for four to five years.
Turf transplants	Heather turves can be transplanted but they have to be obtained from existing heaths, which may be damaged. However, transferring litter and top soil does mimic the ancient practice of turf-cutting (turbary) which was partly responsible for maintaining open heathland in the past. The vegetation is first flailed with a flail mower, the top few centimetres of litter and top soil are rotovated and the loose material is spread on the site to be restored. The site should also be prepared to provide a nutrient-poor sub-soil. The roots and seeds remaining on the donor site regenerate. Where erosion is liable a nurse crop of grasses with a low productivity, such as wavy hair-grass, can be sown at rates of 10–15 kilograms per hectare. Once the heather is established then other heathland plants can be introduced as transplanted pot plants.

6.3   The case studies

The creation of new habitats is not planned in the case study areas. The options for management for conservation purposes are covered in Section 5.4.

Chapter 7

IMPLEMENTATION AND MONITORING

Once you have a clear idea of which management options are feasible on your land, based on your assessment of its quality and potential, the options you choose to put into practice will depend on your objectives and the constraints affecting your use of the land, as described in the foundation book.

If you are unclear or uncertain of what action to take at this, or at any other, stage in the management planning process, it is important to seek professional advice or help. This is most important when the outcomes of the management plan are being transferred to a detailed work plan, describing when and where operations are to be done, who will do the work, the equipment needed, the expected costs and benefits and how the results are to be monitored in the long term.

It is best to keep the work plan simple, so that it is easily understood by other people, but it should provide enough detail to allow the planner to monitor progress and check that particular tasks have been done.

Both a management plan and a work plan should be written before any work is done. Not only will this help clarify the objectives for the planner it will also provide agreed guidelines for the workforce, whether they be your own labour or contractors brought in to do the job. Equally important, grant aid is usually approved on the submission of an appropriate management/work plan and normally before any work is undertaken.

7.1   Grant aid

Each organisation which gives grant aid (see the *Helpful Organisations* booklet in the foundation module) has its own grant conditions. These are designed to ensure that the project is done correctly and that the recipient will fulfil the objectives of the grant-awarding body. You must clearly understand these conditions before applying for grant aid and particularly check whether prior approval is needed for any work. If work has started, the grant aid may be forfeited.

Although there may be several potential sources of grant aid for any one project, generally they are mutually exclusive, i.e. only one grant can be given for an individual project. However, there are exceptions to this. For example, in National Parks additional payments may be available from the National Park Authority to supplement grants under Ministry of Agriculture, Fisheries and Food (MAFF) schemes. Similarly, an extra management grant from The Countryside Commission may be available to supplement MAFF monies provided for set-aside schemes. Always check these details with the grant-awarding organisation.

7.2   Management costs

The major direct costs of managing grassland, heath or moor are livestock, labour and materials, but equipment and the timing of operations are also important. For example, spare labour may be available at particular times of the year, allowing the cost of some operations to be cut, or hiring a contractor who has specialised equipment may be preferable to buying the machines. However, there are also indirect costs in necessary items such as training, insurance and the management costs of grant and planning procedures.

As the costs of various items, particularly livestock, can fluctuate from year to year it is important to have reliable figures on which to base any costings. These can be supplied by advisers of various kinds but two particularly comprehensive sources are Wye College's *Farm Management Pocketbook* and the Scottish Agricultural College's *Farm Management Handbook* (see Appendix I for full details). Both provide information on agricultural and conservation activities, financial matters and current grant schemes.

It is one thing to have the costs for various items, but it is also essential to place those costs in a business management framework, even if wildlife conservation is the priority. This is particularly so for farm business management or related businesses such as country parks and golf courses, where the business has a dynamic nature; there is a need to cope with uncertainty in decision making. There is also a need to deal with situations as they arise, not just with the deployment of resources at a planning level; and the aims are not solely to make a profit. Seasonality, weather, changing prices, the number and size of the enterprises or habitats on a single holding can all lead to a complex situation.

In planning the farm activities, the land manager has to bear all these factors in mind, and will usually try to choose enterprises which will make the greatest contribution to profit, while at the same time fully using the available resources. To do this, the following two techniques can be used.

Gross margin analysis and labour profiles

One of the commonly used techniques is gross margin analysis. The *gross margin* of an enterprise is the value of its output, less its variable costs. These *variable costs* are specific to that enterprise, and vary with the scale of the enterprise. For grass (or arable) crops, the main items making up the variable costs will be fertiliser, seed, sprays for weed and disease control, additional casual labour and contract work done on that crop.

The variable cost items for a livestock enterprise are concentrated feeds and veterinary expenses, and the variable costs attributable to any crops that are grown specially to feed the livestock, such as lucerne or maize grown for silage.

Table 7.1 shows an example of the sort of calculation which is involved in estimating gross margins.

Of course, these are not the only costs that need to be borne. The *fixed costs* are those which relate to the whole farm, and which do not vary with the enterprise adopted, at least over the medium term. They include:

Table 7.1　Gross margin analysis of various sheep systems (average performance level only)

System	Early lambing per ewe	Winter fattening of store lambs per head	Upland flocks per ewe	Hill flocks per ewe
No. of lambs reared per ewe	1.4	–	1.3	1.0
	£	£	£	£
Average price per lamb sold	42.0	41.0	32.5	27.5
Lamb sales	58.8	40.7	42.3	20.6
Ewe premium	8.0	–	8.0	8.0
Wool	3.0	–	2.5	1.7
Subsidy	–	–	4.5	6.7
Sub-total	69.8	40.7	57.3	37.0
LESS Livestock purchases (net of cull sales)	12.8	32.7	10.9	(+) 3.5
OUTPUT	57.0	8.0	46.4	40.5
Variable costs:				
Concentrates	21.0	2.2	6.6	3.9
	(145 kg)	(15 kg)	(45 kg)	(25 kg)
Veterinary and medical	4.0	0.2	3.1	2.4
Miscellaneous and transport	2.0	0.3	1.3	0.9
TOTAL VARIABLE COSTS (excl. forage)	27.0	2.7	12.0	7.2
GROSS MARGIN per ewe (or head) before deducting forage variable costs	30.0	5.3	34.4	33.3
Forage variable costs (incl. bought forage)	6.7	0.8	5.8	3.3
GROSS MARGIN per ewe (or head)	23.3	4.5	28.6	30.0
Stocking rate [no. per forage ha (acre)]	13.5	50	8.65	–
	(5.5)	(20)	(3.5)	
GROSS MARGIN per forage hectare	315	225	247	–
GROSS MARGIN per forage acre	127	90	100	–

(Source: Nix, 1991)

1　rent, or mortgage interest;
2　costs of employed staff;
3　machinery costs;
4　general overheads.

It is important to realise that the gross margin is not a direct measure of the profitability of a farm. It only measures the contribution that each enterprise makes to the general fixed costs of the farm. Profit is the difference between these fixed costs and the sum of the gross margins of all the enterprises. The gross margin can be used as a measure of revenue for the number and range of enterprises on the holding.

To make these planning decisions, the farmer will probably try to 'explore' the likely results of choosing different enterprises, and choose the combination which provides a reasonably high revenue, makes effective use of the available capital, labour and other resources, and does not violate accepted rotational practices or involve too high a level of risk. The farmer is also likely to choose crops or other enterprises which are already familiar, or at least, if unfamiliar enterprises are tried, they will be on only a small scale at first.

This strategy is equally effective where conservation is the priority.

Labour, cash and machinery use are particular problems for the farm or site manager because of the large seasonal variation in the need for these resources. One of the important tasks in planning the enterprises on a farm or site is therefore to ensure that the possible combinations chosen do not result in impossible 'peaks' in the demands made on them.

Labour and machinery allocation can be planned on two levels. First, planning on the *whole farm* level ensures that the farming system makes the best use of labour throughout the year. Inevitably there will be peaks and troughs in the need for labour but, by careful choice of enterprises, use of suitable machinery and of contractors and casual labour, it should be possible to use people and machinery reasonably effectively.

Secondly, planning on the *operational* level involves ensuring that a specific task is done effectively, be it ploughing, silage-making or lambing. To do this the correct equipment, and method of working, is needed which depends on proper training.

Planning labour use at the whole farm level involves preparing a labour profile, showing the number of worker hours required month by month. From such a chart, any major peaks and troughs can be identified. Figure 7.1 is an example of a labour profile for a 250-hectare farm with winter wheat, spring barley, main crop potatoes and sheep.

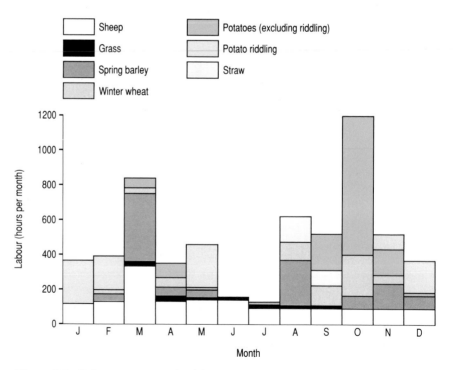

Figure 7.1   Labour use on a mixed farm with several enterprises

110

Livestock

Several economic factors influence the choice of livestock for a site, as well as the wildlife factors. First, there is the size of the site. Anything less than 10 hectares does not usually allow for an economically viable herd of cattle or flock of sheep. It can suffice for horses or ponies where a higher rent may be charged. Secondly, where there are no facilities for livestock, dairy cattle are definitely excluded and even simple facilities like fencing may be too expensive to install. Similar problems arise where there are no permanent members of staff available, although there is the option of finding a local farmer to provide the grazing (see section 7.3 on letting). Thirdly, where dog worrying or vandalism may be a problem, cattle are preferable to sheep. Most of these factors are summarised in Table 5.1.

Another consideration is the stocking rate or density, which varies according to the need, the number of grazing weeks per year, and the type of animal (see Table 7.2).

Materials

The main materials needed on grasslands, heaths and moors are barriers to the movement of grazing animals. The separation of fields by walls, banks, hedges or fences is normal and their subdivision by temporary fences is common. Only in open upland areas or where the stock is tethered or where a shepherd controls the animals is fencing unnecessary. Permanent divisions, providing they do not enclose areas that are too small for modern machinery, are valuable. Keeping them in good repair is important.

Table 7.2   Recommended stocking rates* to maintain wildlife interest

Number of grazing weeks per year	Calcareous grassland		Neutral grassland		Acid grassland		†Marshy grassland
	Sheep	Cattle	Sheep	Cattle	Sheep	Cattle	Cattle
2	60	15	100	25	40	10	12
4	30	8	50	12.5	20	5	6
6	20	5	33	8	12	3	4
8	15	4	25	6	10	2.5	5
10	12	3	20	5	8	2	2.5
12	10	2.5	17	4	8	2	2
14	8.5	2	14	3.5	6	1.5	2
16	7.5	2	12.5	3	6	1.5	1.5
20	6	1.5	10	2.5	4	1	1
24	5	1	8	2	4	1	–
36	3.5	1	5.5	1.5	2	0.5	–
52	2.5	0.5	4	1	2	0.2	–
Grazing pressure (animal weeks/ha/yr)	120 or 30		200 or 50		100 or 25		25

*Expressed as number of animals per hectare. † Sheep are not suitable.

Permanent fences, of wooden post and rail, post and wire or post and wire netting, are commonly used although they are of little wildlife value compared to hedges.

The electric fence has greatly simplified the provision of fencing and reduced its cost. Through a unit powered by mains electricity, batteries or wind or solar generators, an electric pulse of high voltage is generated. This is carried in the fence wire which may be plain wire or woven wire, 1.5–2 millimetres in diameter, or stranded nylon which includes a metal strand. Stranded nylon netting is also available. The animal touching the wire completes the circuit to earth and receives a shock. Electric fences can provide field divisions and subdivisions at low cost. Moreover, they provide an easily movable fence which can be used for rotational or 'strip' grazing.

Animals must be trained to respect electric fences. When first turned out they should be in small enclosures of not more than 0.5 hectares. If a single electric wire is used, it should be made clearly visible by hanging string or other markers on it.

Equipment

The majority of equipment for managing grasslands, heaths and moors is likely to be grass-cutting machinery. The variety of grass-cutting machines available is large. They range from small, hand-operated mowers, through large tractor-powered mowers, to specialised forage harvesters.

1   Conventional cylinder or reel mowers use a scissor-like cutting action and range from single hand-propelled models, 0.36 metres wide or less, to self-propelled/trailed seven unit gangs, up to 6.25 metres wide. They are designed to work with short grass and produce a relatively high quality finish.

2   Rotary and flail mowers both require more power then reel mowers to smash vegetation as they use blunt instruments in a variety of shapes and sizes (in the horizontal and vertical planes respectively) but they can handle long, dense, tangled material. The finely divided product is usually distributed from the rotary mower in swathes which is more likely to smother the sward than the more even spread from the flail mower.

3   Reciprocating finger or cutter bar and single or double knife mowers use the scissor principle, but the former tends to jam with herbage, whereas the latter is self-clearing but more expensive.

4   Disc and drum mowers have knives attached to the bottom edge of devices mounted on floating arms which act as a special type of rotary mower. Designed for silage and hay crops, they have a high work rate but are vulnerable to damage on the ground (especially the discs) and they leave long, coarse, dense swathes which must be removed, possibly after **tedding** to hasten drying.

5   Forage harvesters are ideal for large areas, having a high work rate and the capacity to collect the cuttings, but they are not readily available for urban sites and do not solve the disposal problem.

6   The recently introduced compact-tractor trailed flails, 1.8 metres wide, can cut from 100 down to 10 millimetres and have incorporated pick-up wagons which would be useful in urban areas, although the hopper capacity of 1–2 cubic metres is modest.

Grass cutting always incurs costs and generally produces no income, except where it can be used as hay or silage.

7.3   Legislation

Legislation can have an impact on the management of grasslands, heaths and moors in four ways: there are restrictions on burning; there are regulations governing activities on commons; there are restrictions that follow from designating land for wildlife, landscape or archaeological considerations; and there is legislation covering the letting of land for grazing purposes.

Burning

Moorland burning (also called **muirburn** or **swaling**) is legally restricted to the period between 1 November and 31 March (15 April in the uplands) in England and Wales by the Heather and Grass Burning (England and Wales Regulations, 1985) and to the period between 1 October and 15 April in Scotland by the Hill Farming Act 1946. A licence must be obtained from the relevant government department with responsibilities for agriculture. Extensions are possible to allow burning until 15 May if the moor lies above 457 metres. Special licences can extend the legal muirburn period to allow burning after unsuitable spring weather and summer burning of heather infested by heather beetle.

In addition, 24–72 hours' written notice must be given to neighbours of the intention to burn, and the local NCC office must be consulted where the site is adjacent to an SSSI.

Commons

The general features of legislation covering commons are described in the *Legislation and Regulations* booklet in the foundation module. A particular piece of legislation deals with works on common land. Under the Law of Property Act 1925, Section 194 applications are needed for the erection of fencing, buildings and other works on commons (works and buildings include sports pavilions, bus shelters, car parks, surfaced tracks, ditches, banks and public conveniences).

Section 194 applies to most common land registered under the Commons Registration Act 1965, with the following exceptions:

▶   land which was not subject to rights of common on 1 January 1926 – unless there is evidence to the contrary you should assume that, if the land is registered under the 1965 Act, it was subject to rights in 1926;

▶   land over which rights of common have been extinguished by statute;

▶   land over which rights of common have been extinguished by other means than by statute and where the Secretary of State has approved exclusion of the land from Section 194.

Also, Section 194 does not apply to works if they are authorised by an Act of Parliament, or erected in connection with mineral extraction or telephone lines. Section 194 does not provide for exchange land to be given where works reduce the area of common. If an authority wants to give exchange land, it may have to go through the compulsory purchase procedure under the Acquisition of Land Act 1981. Further details can be provided by the Open Spaces Society or the Department of Environment (see the *Helpful Organisations* booklet in the foundation module).

Designation

Full details of the current types of designation of land and their implications are given in the *Legislation* and *Regulations* booklet in the foundation module.

There are three types of arrangement for managing grassland sites:

1   it can be grazed or cut using livestock and machinery owned by those responsible for managing the site;

2   it can be grazed or cut under a short-term licence which can be changed at yearly intervals if necessary;

3   a full agricultural tenancy can be created whereby the tenant has security of tenure and, within the terms of the tenancy, control over the management and use of the grassland.

The advantages and disadvantages of each type of tenure are discussed below, but professional advice from experienced land agents is essential. Advice is also available from the local Ministry of Agriculture Officer.

Own management   The main advantage of managing with your own livestock or machinery is that you have complete control over management as regards the timing and intensity of grazing or cutting and, at the same time, the opportunity of generating income. On the other hand, substantial amounts of money are required for buying livestock, for maintaining fences, for labour to look after the animals, and so on, which must be set against the income that will probably be generated by the enterprise.

Short-term licence   A short-term tenancy (up to 364 days) for grazing or mowing is much favoured as it gives the land manager a degree of control over the tenant in the year in which the licence is granted and, furthermore, it enables the management to be changed yearly if necessary. It is recommended particularly for its flexibility and as a source of income with little capital expenditure by the land manager. The disadvantages are that the terms of the licence have to be negotiated and renewed each year; the income derived from a licence, especially if there are many restrictions, is likely to be low; the owners may incur maintenance costs which might not be their responsibility if a full tenancy was operated; there is the danger that granting a succession of 364-day grazing licences will be seen as creating a tenancy under the Agricultural Holdings Acts of 1948 and 1984.

Full agricultural tenancy   Once established, a full agricultural tenancy cannot be altered without the agreement of the tenants and they are unlikely to consent to change unless they benefit from a new agreement. Some sites will already have full agricultural tenants present, and, in many cases, these have created problems in the conservation management of the site. On the other hand, bodies such as the National Trust, which have many years' experience in managing properties and land to which the public have access, find that a full agricultural tenancy is beneficial, providing the terms of the agreement are carefully drawn up.   A clause can be included in the agreement enabling possession to be regained for specified non-agricultural purposes or to ensure that conservation measures are undertaken.

Experience has shown that it is better to invite tenders only from local farmers, to make the agreement with well-established, successful farmers and, once a relationship has been established, to offer the licence each year to the same farmer.

7.4   Monitoring

Both management plans and work plans are a statement of what the landowner or land manager would like to see happen to the site. For various reasons the work plan might not be fulfilled, for example staff are off sick at a critical time, or it may have an unexpected outcome, for example newly sown grassland dies after a very dry spring and needs replacing. Such problems are always likely to happen but, if possible, try to turn round a *problem* to provide an *opportunity* to increase the conservation value of the area.

Having produced a management plan it will be easier to cope with unexpected events and to adapt the plan to incorporate them. There is therefore a need to monitor developments, ranging from several times a year to every five years, to be able to recognise and act on any changes. If wildlife conservation is a primary objective, annual surveys may be all that is required to monitor the gradual development or improvement of the site. Indeed, when grant aid is given, regular reviews of progress during and at the end of an approved period may be required as a condition of the grant, although monitoring should be seen as an enjoyable task rather than a burden.

Finally, the information from monitoring should feed directly into the management planning cycle, since management plans should not be one-off tablets of stone but continually evolving records of achievement of the maintenance, enhancement and creation of valued landscapes and wildlife habitats.

7.5   Monitoring of the case study areas

Borders hill farm

No matter what technique is used to improve the quality and cover of heather on a farm, some form of monitoring is required to assess the success of the changes in management.

A study of aerial photographs from 1946 and 1988 was useful for an overall study of the farm. They showed a decrease in heather cover on certain areas. However, the interpretation of more detailed information on bracken/acidic grassland expansion requires more experience in identifying the subtle differences in contrast. Also, acquiring photographs from particular years is often costly. The land manager's own photographic record from permanent markers, e.g. fence posts, cairns, etc., around the farm can act as a base-line from which to monitor how future changes in management will manifest themselves. The other method is a means of quantifying observations from the photographic record and identifying more quickly a deterioration in the system. During the period March to May selected heather types that are vulnerable to grazing pressures, e.g. young heather, old heather, heather near feeding points, etc., can be surveyed. By walking five transect lines per heather type the proportion of current heather leading shoots which have been grazed can be estimated. If this is more than 65% (i.e. two-thirds) then the area is recorded as overgrazed. If an assessment of the growth form of the heather in these species fits into either carpet, topiary or drumstick heather the area is recorded as chronically heavily grazed. To obtain a picture of the more widespread grazing pressures the sites should be checked in July or August for general features such as heather grazing, grass sward height and the types of grasses grazed, especially mat grass and purple moor-grass. These results need to be collated over several years to see the average variation in grass and heather growth from year to year.

Stelling Minnis Common

As the development of the management plan is still incomplete, little thought has been given to how to monitor developments on the Common. The Managers do see it as an essential item, given the wide range of interests involved.

115

FURTHER READING

The following list includes books that we recommend as further reading. Those marked with an asterisk were used as sources when writing this book.

*Anon (1988) *Heathland Restoration: a Handbook of Techniques*. British Gas, Southampton

*Anon (1990a) *On Course Conservation: Managing Golf's Natural Heritage*. Nature Conservancy Council, Peterborough

*Anon (1990b) *Wild Flowers and Grass Seed Mixtures for Habitat Creation, Landscaping and General Ground Cover*. Phytomer Seeds, King's Lynn

*Anon (1991) *Wild Flower Manual*. Johnson's Seeds, Boston

*Butterflies Under Threat Team (1986) *The Management of Chalk Grassland for Butterflies*. Nature Conservancy Council, Peterborough

*Chadwick, L (1991) *Farm Management Handbook*, 12th edn. Scottish Agricultural College, Edinburgh

*Daniels, J L (1985) *Heathland Management Trials at Brindley Heath*. CCP 183, Technical Report 2. Countryside Commission, Cheltenham

Davidson, J, Lloyd, R (1977) *Conservation and Agriculture*. John Wiley, London

Duffey, E, Morris, M G, Sheail, J, Ward, L K, Wells, D A, Wells, T C E (1974) *Grassland Ecology and Wildlife Management*. Chapman and Hall, London

Fitter, R, Fitter, A, Blamey, M (1978) *The Wild Flowers of Britain and Northern Europe*. Collins, London

*Fry, R, Lonsdale, D (eds) (1991) *Habitat Conservation for Insects – a Neglected Green Issue*. The Amateur Entomologists' Society, Middlesex

Gair, R (1988) *Farm Conservation Guide*. Schering Agriculture, Nottingham

Green, B H (1985) *Countryside Conservation*, 2nd edn. George Allen and Unwin, London

*Holmes, W (ed) (1989) *Grass: Its Production and Utilisation*, 2nd edn. Blackwell, Oxford

Hubbard, C E (1968) *Grasses*, 2nd edn. Penguin Books, Harmondsworth

Lockhart, J A R, Wiseman, A J L (1988) *Intoduction to Crop Husbandry Including Grassland*, 6th edn. Pergamon Press, Oxford

*Lowday, J E, Wells, T C E (1977) *The Management of Grassland and Heathland in Country Parks*, CCP 105. Countryside Commission, Cheltenham

*MacDonald, A (1990) *Heather Damage: a Guide to Types of Damage and Their Causes*. Nature Conservancy Council, Peterborough

*Morris, P (ed) (1980) *Natural History of the British Isles*. Country Life Books, Richmond

*Mowforth, M A, Sydes, S (1989) *Moorland Management: a Literature Review*. Nature Conservancy Council, Peterborough

*Nix, J (1991) *Farm Management Pocketbook*, 21st edn. Wye College, Ashford

Nix, J, Hill, P, Williams, N (1987) *Land and Estate Management*. Packard Publishing, Chichester

Rackham, O (1986) *The History of the Countryside*. J M Dent and Sons Ltd, London

Rowell, T A (1988) *The Peatland Management Handbook*. Nature Conservancy Council, Peterborough

*The Open University (1986) *S326 Ecology*. Third-level undergraduate course texts. Open University Press, Milton Keynes

*The Open University (1987) *T274 Food Production Systems*. Second-level undergraduate course texts. Open University Press, Milton Keynes

Webb, N (1986) *Heathlands*. Collins, London

*Wells, T C E, Sheail, J (1988) The effects of agricultural change on the wildlife interest of lowland grasslands. In: Park, J R (ed) *Environmental Management in Agriculture*, 186–201. Belhaven Press, London

*Wells, T C E, Cox, R, Frost, A (1989) *The Establishment and Management of Wildflower Meadows*. Nature Conservancy Council, Peterborough

*Wells, T C E, Frost, A, Bell, S (1986) *Wildflower Grasslands from Crop-grown Seed and Hay Bales*. Nature Conservancy Council, Peterborough

GLOSSARY

Acidic This term refers to soils, and the plant communities which they support, that have a low *pH*, e.g. acidic grassland.

Alkaline This terms refers to soils, and the plant communities which they support, that are of a *calcareous* nature and have a high *pH*, e.g. chalk downland.

Biomass The weight of all the organisms forming a given population or inhabiting a given area.

Blanket bog An area of extensive, acid, wet, springy, flat and gently sloping ground consisting of vegetation in a state of arrested decomposition. The other main categories of bog are basin, raised and valley bogs.

Brace A pair of game birds.

Brash Small branches trimmed from the sides and top of the trunk of a tree. Also known as lop and top or slash.

Cairn A mound of stones erected as a memorial or marker.

Calcareous Made of, or containing, calcium carbonate and therefore alkaline.

Calcicole A plant that thrives on *calcareous* or *alkaline* soils, such as those on chalk or limestone.

Climax community The end point of an undisturbed *succession* under the prevailing climatic and soil conditions. Natural events or human activities can cause arrested climax communities by influencing the succession.

Conservation The careful management of wildlife habitats. The keeping of cut grass as either hay or silage as overwintering fodder for livestock.

Cull To remove an animal, especially an inferior one, from a herd.

Cultivar A variety of a plant produced from a natural species and maintained by cultivation.

D-value A measure of the digestibility of grass. The nutritive value is directly proportional to the D-value.

Earthwork Soil-covered archaeological remains visible as undulations on the land surface.

Ericaceous Belonging to the *Ericaceae*, a family of trees and shrubs with typically bell-shaped flowers.

Flood meadow Where rivers periodically spread out over their lowland plains covering them with alluvium.

Hay Grass that is cut and dried as fodder first in rows or swathes, then by turning or *tedding* and finally made into bales.

Headland Area at the end of a field where cultivation machinery is turned around and which has to be cultivated separately from the main body of the field.

Heath A large open area, usually with sandy soil and scrubby vegetation, especially heather, normally at low altitudes.

Hydroseeding A process by which seeds are applied to an embankment or cutting by spraying with a mixture of water and bulky organic material.

Improved grassland Grassland that has been re-seeded and/or treated with fertiliser and sometimes pesticides in order to boost productivity.

In-bye land On a hill farm, it is the land close to the farmhouse, generally improved pasture.

Legume A plant belonging to the family *Leguminosae* which can fix nitrogen in the soil.

Ley Arable land temporarily under grass.

Loam Fertile soil composed of various mixtures of different sized particles.

Lynchet A terrace or ridge formed in prehistoric or medieval times by ploughing a hillside.

Meadow An area of grassland used for producing hay or sometimes for grazing animals.

Mire An area of permanently wet peat.

Moor An upland area of open, unenclosed ground usually covered with heather, coarse grasses, bracken and moss.

Muirburn The burning of heather moorland. Also known as swaling.

Neutral Soil that is neither *acidic* nor *alkaline*.

Niche The status of a plant or animal within its community, which determines its activities and relationships with other organisms and its environment.

Pasture Land covered with grass or herbage and grazed by or suitable for grazing by livestock.

Permanent grassland An area that remains grassland for five or more years.

pH A quantitative expression for the acidity or alkalinity of a solution or soil. The scale ranges from 0 to 15: pH 7 is neutral, less than 7 is acidic, more than 7 is alkaline

Poaching The break-up of land into wet muddy patches usually by animals.

Provenance The place of origin of seeds or plants, which remains the same no matter where later generations of plants are raised.

Rhizome An underground stem which helps a plant to either survive the winter and/or to reproduce vegetatively.

Ridge and furrow Regular undulations still visible in some old *pastures*, usually an indication of medieval strip cultivation.

Ruminant A mammal which chews the cud and has a four-chambered stomach, e.g. deer, cattle, sheep, goats.

Scrub An area dominated by shrubs, possibly as a stage in the *succession* to woodland.

Semi-natural An assemblage of native species that is apparently natural but has been modified by human activities.

Silage Any crop harvested while green for fodder and kept succulent by partial fermentation in a silo or clamp.

Siliceous Soils containing silica.

Succession The replacement of one kind of community by another, shown by the progressive changes in vegetation that may culminate in a *climax community*. Successions developing on new surfaces are primary successions; those developing on disturbed surfaces are secondary successions.

Swaling See *muirburn*

Sward A stretch of turf or grassy vegetation.

Tedding The turning of hay to dry it.

Tiller A side-shoot of grass, arising at ground level.

Turf The surface layer of fields and *pastures*, consisting of earth containing a dense growth of grasses with their roots.

Unimproved grassland Grassland that has not been re-seeded or treated with chemical fertiliser or pesticides.

Vegetative reproduction Reproduction by plants by asexual processes such as runners, cuttings or fragments of the parent plant.

Washlands Washlands or washes are artificial *flood meadows* created for drainage or flood control purposes.

Water meadows An artificial *flood meadow* found in certain chalk stream valleys in Wiltshire, Hampshire and Dorset.

SCIENTIFIC NAMES FOR WILDLIFE SPECIES

Plants

Agrimony *Agrimonia eupatoria*

Alder *Alnus glutinosa*

Alder buckthorn *Frangula alnus*

Alpine bearberry *Arctostaphylos uva-ursi*

Amphibious bistort *Polygonum amphibium*

Annual knawel *Scleranthus annuus*

Ash *Fraxinus excelsior*

Aspen *Populus tremula*

Bastard toadflax *Thesium humifusum*

Bedstraw,
  Heath *Galium saxatile*
  Lady's *Galium verum*
  Marsh *Galium palustre*
  Slender *Galium pumilum*

Bell heather *Erica cinerea*

Bent grasses *Agrostis* spp

Betony *Stachys officinalis*

Bilberry *Vaccinium myrtillus*

Birch trees *Betula* spp

Black medick *Medicago lupulina*

Blackcurrant *Ribes nigrum*

Blackthorn *Prunus spinosa*

Bog asphodel *Narthecium ossifragum*

Bog myrtle *Myrica gale*

Bog rosemary *Andromeda polifolia*

Bogbean *Menyanthes trifoliata*

Bracken *Pteridium aquilinum*

Bramble *Rubus fruticosus*

Branched bur-reed *Sparganium erectum*

Broad-leaved dock *Rumex obtusifolius*

Brome,
  Meadow *Bromus commutatus*
  Upright *Bromus erectus*

Broom *Cytisus scoparius*

Buckthorn *Rhamnus catharticus*

Burnet,
  Great *Sanguisorba officinalis*
  Salad *Sanguisorba minor*

Buttercup,
  Bulbous *Ranunculus bulbosus*
  Creeping *Ranunculus repens*
  Meadow *Ranunculus acris*

Cambridge milk parsley *Selinum carvifolia*

Carrot,
  Moon *Seseli libanotis*
  Wild *Daucus carota*

Catchfly,
  Nottingham *Silene nutans*
  Sticky *Lychnis viscaria*

Catsear,
  Common *Hypochaeris radicata*
  Spotted *Hypochaeris maculata*

Charlock *Sinapis arvensis*

Chickweed,
  Common *Stellaria media*
  Water *Myosoton aquaticum*

Cinquefoil,
  Hoary *Potentilla argentea*
  Marsh *Potentilla palustris*
  Spring *Potentilla tabernaemontani*

Clover,
  Haresfoot *Trifolium arvense*
  Sulphur *Trifolium ochroleuchon*

Clustered bellflower *Campanula glomerata*

Cocksfoot grass *Dactylis glomerata*

Common bent *Agrostis tenuis*

Common comfrey *Symphytum officinale*

Common cudweed *Filago vulgaris*

Common mouse-ear *Cerastium fontanum*

Common storksbill *Erodium cicutarium*

Cotton grass *Eriophorum vaginatum*

Couch grass *Agropyron repens*

Cowslip *Primula veris*

Cranberry *Vaccinium oxycoccos*

Cranesbill,
  Dovesfoot *Geranium molle*
  Long-stalked *Geranium columbinum*
  Meadow *Geranium pratense*
  Small-flowered *Geranium pusillum*
  Wood *Geranium sylvaticum*

Crested dogstail *Cynosurus cristatus*

Cross-leaved heath *Erica tetralix*

Crowberry *Empetrum nigrum*

Cut-leaved germander *Teucrium botrys*

Daisy *Bellis perennis*

Dandelion *Taraxacum officinale*

Dogwood *Cornus sanguinea*

Dropwort *Filipendula vulgaris*

Dwarf cornel *Cornus suecica*

Dyer's greenweed *Genista tinctoria*

Elder *Sambucus nigra*

Fairy flax *Linum catharticum*

False oat *Arrhenatherum elatius*

Fescue,
  Chewings *Festuca rubra* ssp *commutata*
  Dwarf creeping *Festuca rubra* ssp *litoralis*
  Fine-leaved sheep's *Festuca tenuifolia*
  Red *Festuca rubra* ssp *rubra*
  Sheep's *Festuca ovina*
  Tall *Festuca arundinacea*

Field fleawort *Senecio integrifolius*

Field maple *Acer campestre*

Fine bent *Agrostis tenuis*

Forget-me-not,
  Changing *Myosotis discolor*
  Water *Myosotis scorpoides*

Foxglove *Digitalis purpurea*

Fritillary *Fritillaria meleagris*

Fumitories *Fumaria* spp

Gentian,
  Autumn *Gentianella amarella*
  Chiltern *Gentianella germanica*
  Early *Gentianella anglica*
  Marsh *Gentiana pneumonanthe*

Goatsbeard *Tragopogon pratensis*

Golden oatgrass *Trisetum flavescens*

Goldilocks *Aster linosyris*

Gorse *Ulex europaeus*

Grass of Parnassus *Parnassia palustris*

Great pignut *Bunium bulbocastanum*

Great willow-herb *Epilobium hirsutum*

Greater hawkbit *Leontodon hispidus*

Ground pine *Ajuga chamaepitys*

Groundsel *Senecio vulgaris*

Hair-grass,
  Bog *Deschampsia setacea*
  Silvery *Aira caryophyllea*
  Tufted *Deschampsia caespitosa*
  Wavy *Deschampsia flexuosa*

Hard fern *Blechnum spicant*

Harebell *Campanula rotundifolia*

Hawthorns *Crataegus* spp

Hazel *Corylus avellana*

Heath,
  Cornish *Erica vagans*
  Dorset *Erica ciliaris*

Heath lobelia *Lobelia urens*

Heather (ling) *Calluna vulgaris*

Helleborine,
  Dark-red *Epipactis atrorubens*
  Marsh *Epipactis palustris*

Holly *Ilex aquifolium*

Honewort *Trinia glauca*

Hornbeam *Carpinus betulus*

Hutchinsia *Homungia petraea*

Juniper *Juniperus communis*

Knapweed,
  Black *Centaurea nigra*
  Greater *Centaurea scabiosa*
  Lesser *Centaurea nigra*

Lesser meadow rue *Thalictrum minus* ssp *minus*

Lesser stitchwort *Stellaria graminea*

Ling (heather) *Calluna vulgaris*

Loosestrife,
  Purple *Lythrum salicaria*
  Yellow *Lysimachia vulgaris*

Lousewort,
  Common *Pedicularis sylvatica*
  Marsh *Pedicularis palustris*

Marsh clubmoss *Lycopodium inundatum*

Marsh marigold *Caltha palustris*

Marsh pea *Lathyrus palustris*

Marsh pennywort *Hydrocotyle vulgaris*

Marsh St John's wort *Hypericum elodes*

Marsh valerian *Valeriana dioica*

Mat grass *Nardus stricta*

Meadow barley *Hordeum secalinum*

Meadow clary *Salvia pratensis*

Meadow foxtail *Alopecurus pratensis*

Meadow-grass,
  Rough-stalked *Poa trivialis*
  Smooth-stalked *Poa pratensis*

Meadowsweet *Filipendula vulgaris*

Midland hawthorn *Crataegus laevigata*

Milk parsley *Peucedanum palustre*

Milkwort,
  Chalk *Polygala calcarea*
  Dwarf *Polygala amarella*
  Heath *Polygala serpyllifolia*

Mountain everlasting *Antennaria dioica*

Mountain fern *Oreopteris limbosperma*

Mouse-ear hawkweed *Hieracium pilosella*

Musk mallow *Malva moschata*

Nettles *Urtica* spp

Oaks *Quercus* spp

Orchid,
  Bee *Ophrys apifera*
  Bog *Malaxis paludosa*
  Burnt *Orchis ustulata*
  Common spotted *Dactylorhiza fuchsii*
  Coral-root *Corallorhiza trifida*
  Early marsh *Dactylorhiza incarnata*
  Early purple *Orchis mascula*
  Early spider *Ophrys sphegodes*
  Fen *Liparis loeselii*

Fragrant *Gymnadenia conopsea*
Greater butterfly *Platanthera chlorantha*
Heath spotted *Dactylorhiza maculata*
Late spider *Ophrys fuciflora*
Lesser butterfly *Platanthera bifolia*
Lizard *Himantoglossum hircinum*
Man *Aceras anthropophorum*
Military *Orchis militaris*
Monkey *Orchis simia*
Musk orchid *Herminium monorchis*
Pyramidal *Anacamptis pyramidalis*

Ox-eye daisy *Leucanthemum vulgare*

Oxlip *Primula elatior*

Pasque flower *Pulsatilla vulgaris*

Penny-cress,
  Alpine *Thlaspi alpestre*
  Perfoliate *Thlaspi perfoliatum*

Perennial flax *Linum anglicum*

Perennial rye-grass *Lolium perenne*

Pignut *Conopodium majus*

Pillwort *Pilularia globulifera*

Pines *Pinus* spp

Pink,
  Cheddar *Dianthus gratianopolitanus*
  Maiden *Dianthus deltoides*

Plantain,
  Hoary *Plantago media*
  Ribwort *Plantago lanceolata*

Pondweed,
  Bog *Potamogeton polygonifolius*
  Broad-leaved *Potamogeton natans*

Poppies *Papaver* spp

Purple moor-grass *Molinia caerulea*

Quaking grass *Briza media*

Ragged robin *Lychnis flos-cuculi*

Red dead-nettle *Lamium purpureum*

Reedmaces *Typha* spp

Restharrow *Ononis repens*

Restharrow,
  Small *Ononis reclinata*
  Spiny *Ononis spinosa*

Rhododendron *Rhododendron ponticum*

Rock-cress,
  Bristol *Arabis stricta*
  Hairy *Arabis hirsuta*

Rock-rose,
  Common *Helianthemum chamaecistus*
  Hoary *Helianthemum canum*
  White *Helianthemum apenninum*

Rose,
  Dog *Rosa canina*
  Downy *Rosa tomentosa*
  Guelder *Viburnum opulus*

Rough hawkbit *Leontodon hispidus*

Round-headed leek *Allium sphaerocephalon*

Rowan *Sorbus aucuparia*

Rush,
  Heath *Juncus squarrosus*
  Sharp-flowered *Juncus acutiforus*
  Soft *Juncus effusus*

Sainfoin *Onobrychis viciifolia*

Sand spurrey *Spergularia rubra*

Saxifrage,
  Burnet *Pimpinella saxifraga*
  Meadow *Saxifraga granulata*
  Pepper *Silaum silaus*

Saw-wort *Serratula tinctoria*

Scabious,
  Devil's-bit *Succisa pratensis*
  Field *Knautia arvensis*
  Small *Scabiosa columbaria*

  Scarlet pimpernel *Anagallis arvensis*

Scentless mayweed *Matricaria perforata*

Sedge,
  Bird's-foot *Carex ornithopoda*
  Brown beak *Rhynchospora fusca*
  Downy-fruited *Carex filiformis*
  Dwarf *Carex humilus*
  Heath *Carex ericetorum*

Self-heal *Prunella vulgaris*

Sheep's sorrel *Rumex acetosella*

Shepherd's cress *Teesdalia nudicaulis*

Shepherd's purse *Capsella bursa-pastoris*

Smaller catstail *Phleum bertolonii*

Smooth hawksbeard *Crepis capillaris*

Smooth tare *Vicia tetrasperma*

Somerset grass *Koeleria vallesiana*

Sorrel *Rumex acetosa*

Spearwort,
  Adders tongue *Ranunculus ophioglossifolius*
  Greater *Ranunculus lingua*
  Lesser *Ranunculus flammula*

Speedwell,
  Common field *Veronica persica*
  Germander *Veronica chamaedrys*
  Spiked *Veronica spicata*

Spiked rampion *Phyteuma tenerum*

Spindle tree *Euonymus europaeus*

Spring sandwort *Minuartia verna*

Stone bramble *Rubus saxatilis*

Stonecrop,
  Mossy *Crassula tillaea*
  Rock *Sedum forsteranum*

Summer snowflake *Leucojum aestivum*

Sundews *Drosera* spp

Sweet briar *Rosa rubiginosa*

Sweet vernal-grass *Anthoxanthum odoratum*

Thistle,
  Dwarf *Cirsium acaule*
  Marsh *Cirsium palustre*
  Tuberous *Cirsium tuberosum*

Thyme,
  Large *Thymus pulegioides*
  Wild *Thymus serpyllum*

Timothy *Phleum nodosum*

Tormentil *Potentilla erecta*

Traveller's joy *Clematis vitalba*

Trefoil,
  Birdsfoot *Lotus corniculatus*
  Hop *Trifolium campestre*
  Lesser *Trifolium dubium*

Vetch,
  Common *Vicia sativa*
  Horseshoe *Hippocrepis comosa*
  Kidney *Anthyllis vulneraria*
  Tufted *Vicia cracca*
  Upright *Vicia orobus*

Violet,
  Hairy *Viola hirta*
  Heath dog *Viola canina*
  Marsh *Viola palustris*

Viper's grass *Scorzonera humilis*

Wallflower *Cheiranthus cheiri*

Water dropwort,
  Corky-fruited *Oenanthe pimpinelloides*
  Narrow-leaved *Oenanthe siliafolia*

Wayfaring tree *Viburnum lantana*

Western gorse *Ulex gallii*

White campion *Silene alba*

Whitlow grass *Erophila verna*

Whorled caraway *Carum verticillatum*

Wild basil *Clinopodium vulgare*

Wild candytuft *Iberis amara*

Wild marjoram *Origanum vulgare*

Wild privet *Ligustrum vulgare*

Willow,
  Creeping *Salix repens*
  Eared *Salix aurita*
  Goat *Salix caprea*
  Grey *Salix cinerea*

Wood rushes *Luzula* spp

Wood sage *Teucrium scorodonia*

Yarrow *Achillea millefolium*

Yellow centaury *Cicendia filiformis*

Yellow iris *Iris pseudacorus*

Yellow rattle *Rhinanthus minor*

Yellow star-of-Bethlehem *Gaggea lutea*

Yorkshire fog *Holcus lanatus*

Animals

Adder *Vipera berus*

Argus,
  Brown *Aricia agestis*
  Northern brown *Aricia artaxerxes* ssp *artaxerxes*
  Scotch *Erebia aethiops*

Badger *Meles meles*

Blue,
  Adonis *Lysandra bellargus*
  Chalk-hill *Lysandra coridon*
  Common *Polyommatus icarus*
  Silver-studded *Plebejus argus*
  Small *Cupido minimus*

Brown,
  Meadow *Maniola jurtina*
  Wall *Lasiommata megera*

Buzzard *Buteo buteo*

Carrion crow *Corvus corone* ssp *corone*

Common heath moth *Ematurga atomaria*

Curlew *Numenius arquata*

Dartford warbler *Sylvia undata*

Deer,
  Fallow *Dama dama*
  Red *Cervus elephas*

Dotterel *Endromias morinellus*

Dunlin *Calidris alpina*

Emperor moth *Saturnia pavonia*

Fox *Vulpes vulpes*

Fritillary,
  Dark green *Mesoacidalia aglaia*
  Duke of Burgundy *Hamaeris lucina*
  Glanville *Melitaea cinxia*
  Marsh *Eurodryas aurinia*

Gatekeeper *Pyronia tithonus*

Golden eagle *Aquila chrysaetos*

Golden plover *Pluvialis apricaria*

Grass emerald moth *Pseudoterpna pruinata*

Grasshopper warbler *Locustella naevia*

Grayling *Hipparchia semele*

Green hairstreak *Callophrys rubi*

Green tiger beetle *Cicindela campestris*

Green woodpecker *Picus viridis*

Greenshank *Tringa nebularia*

Grouse,
  Black *Tetrao tetrix*
  Red *Lagopus lagopus* ssp *scoticus*

Hare,
  Brown *Lepus capensis*
  Mountain *Lepus timidus*

Heath assassin bug *Coranus subapterus*

Heath,
  Large *Coenonympha tullia*
  Small *Coenonympha pamphilus*

Heather beetle *Lochmaea suturalis*

Hen harrier *Circus cyaneus*

Hobby *Falco subbuteo*

Kestrel *Falco tinnunculus*

Lapwing *Vanellus vanellus*

Lesser whitethroat *Sylvia curruca*

Linnet *Acanthis cannabina*

Marbled white *Melanargia galathea*

Meadow pipit *Anthus pratensis*

Merlin *Falco columbarius*

Mottled grasshopper *Myrmeleotettix maculatus*

Mountain ringlet *Erebia epiphron*

Mouse,
  Wood *Apodemus sylvaticus*
  Yellow-necked *Sylvaemus flavicollis*

Netted mountain moth *Semiothisa carbonaria*

Nightjar *Caprimulgus europaeus*

Northern eggar moth *Lasiocampa quercus* ssp *callunae*

Orange-tip *Anthocharis cardamines*

Owl,
  Barn *Tyto alba*
  Little *Athene noctua*

Partridge,
  Grey *Perdix perdix*
  Red-legged *Alectoris rufa*

Peregrine *Falco peregrinus*

Pheasant *Phasianus colchicus*

Rabbit *Oryctolagus cuniculus*

Rannoch sprawler moth *Brachionycha sphinx*

Raven *Corvus corax*

Red admiral *Vanessa atalanta*

Red-backed shrike *Lanius collurio*

Redshank *Tringa totanus*

Ring ouzel *Turdus torquatus*

Ringlet *Aphantopus hyperantus*

Sand lizard *Lacerta agilis*

Short-tailed vole *Microtus agrestis*

Shrew,
  Common *Sorex araneus*
  Pygmy *Sorex minutus*

Skipper,
  Chequered *Carterocephalus palaemon*
  Dingy *Erynnis tages*
  Essex *Thymelicus lineola*
  Large *Ochlodes venatus*
  Lulworth *Thymelicus acteon*

  Silver-spotted *Hesperia comma*
  Small *Thymelicus flavus*

Skylark *Alauda arvensis*

Slow worm *Anguis fragilis*

Small copper *Lycaena phlaeas*

Smooth snake *Coronella austriaca*

Snipe *Gallinago gallinago*

Stone curlew *Burhinus oedicnemus*

Stonechat *Saxicola torquata*

Swallow *Hirundo rustica*

Swallowtail *Papilio machaon*

Toad *Bufo bufo*

Tree pipit *Anthus trivialis*

Twite *Acanthis flavirostris*

Weasel *Mustela nivalis*

Wheatear *Oenanthe oenanthe*

Whitethroat *Sylvia communis*

Yellow wagtail *Motacilla flava*

Acknowledgements

The Open University Course Team is greatly indebted to the many people, with a wide range of experience of countryside management, who have contributed to the development of this teaching programme.

First, we must acknowledge the very generous financial support for the whole programme given by the Nature Conservancy Council, along with the Esmée Fairbairn Charitable Trust and the Ernest Cook Trust, and the support given for this particular module by British Gas.

Secondly, we also value the comments and support of the external assessor, Professor B Green, The Sir Cyril Kleinwort Professor of Countryside Management, Wye College, University of London.

Thirdly, we are extremely grateful to the two consultants who helped with the case studies: C Buist (FFWAG adviser, Borders) and P Cobb (FWAG adviser, Kent), as well as the many residents of Stelling Minnis who participated in a special workshop.

Finally, we would like to thank the many other people who provided some material for the book or read and commented on preliminary drafts:

S Carr (Open University)
K Groeneveld (Open Spaces Society)
T Hammond (Nature Conservancy Council for England)
W Lutley (Open Spaces Society)
J Mackintosh (Nature Conservancy Council for Scotland)
R Marrs (Liverpool University)
J Milne (Macaulay Land Use Research Institute)
R Morris (Open University)
T Rowell (Ecological Consultant)
J Tallowin (AFRC Institute of Grassland and Environmental Research)
T Watt (Wye College, University of London).

Grateful acknowledgement is made to the following sources for permission to use material in this book:

Figures
Figures 3.1, 3.2 and 3.3: P. Morris, *Natural History of the British Isles*, 1980, Midsummer Books; Figure 3.4: *The Reader's Digest Complete Atlas of the British Isles*, 1965, Reader's Digest Association Ltd; Figures 3.6 and 4.5: A. MacDonald, *Report: No 28 – Heather Damage: A Guide to Types of Damage and Their Causes*, 1990, Nature Conservancy Council.

Tables
Table 3.4: T.C.E. Wells and J. Sheail 'The effects of agricultural change on the wildlife interest of lowland grasslands', in J.R. Park (ed), *Environmental Management in Agriculture*, 1988, Belhaven Press; Table 5.1: J.E. Lowday and T.C.E. Wells, *The Management of Grassland and Heathland in Country Parks*, 1977, Countryside Commission; Table 5.4: J.L. Daniels, *Heathland Management Trials at Brindley Heath*, 1985, Countryside Commission; Table 6.1: T.C.E. Wells, R. Cox and A. Frost, *The Establishment and Management of Wildflower Meadows*, 1989, Nature Conservancy Council; Table 6.2: The Amateur Entomologists' Society, 22 Salisbury Road, Feltham, Middlesex; Table 6.3: Phytomer Seeds; Table 7.1: J. Nix with P. Hill, *Farm Management Pocketbook*, 1990, 21st edition, Wye College. Reproduced by permission of John Nix.

Index